Reading of Arete Classic I
Demian
데미안

Reading of Arete Classic I: Demian (데미안)

발　행 | 2023년 12월 4일
저　자 | 한학선
펴낸이 | 한건희
펴낸곳 | 주식회사 부크크
출판사등록 | 2014.07.15.(제2014-16호)
주　소 | 서울특별시 금천구 가산디지털1로 119 SK트윈타워 A동 305호
전　화 | 1670-8316
이메일 | info@bookk.co.kr

ISBN | 979-11-410-5706-0

www.bookk.co.kr

Demian

-I listen to the teachings my blood whispers to me.-

CONTENTS

전하고 싶은 말

여러분은 영어 고전을 읽고 감동해서 울어본 적이 있나요? 영어를 그렇게 잘 하는 사람이 아니라면 영어고전을 완벽하게 이해하고 감동의 눈물을 흘리기란 어려울 것입니다. 그리고 고전 작품들 중에서 우리가 마음 깊숙한 곳에서 공감을 느껴 눈물을 흘리게 할 만한 작품은 그리 많지 않습니다. 그 이유는 작품들은 우수하지만 문화가 다르고, 시대가 다르기 때문에 공감의 폭이 그 만큼 줄어들기 때문일 지도 모릅니다.

『데미안』이란 작품에 앞서 니체의 『차라투스트라는 이렇게 말했다』를 읽고 대학생들을 대상으로 아레테 고전강독을 수업으로 진행했습니다. 수업을 진행하면서 점점 더 니체의 사상에 매료되었기에, 좀 더 쉬운 작품으로 니체의 '위버멘쉬'나 '아모르파티' 그리고 '영원회귀'와 같은 사상들을 전해줄 책을 없을까? 생각했습니다. 그때 젊은 시절에 읽었던 『데미안』의 번역본이 빛이 바래어 나의 서재의 책장 모퉁이에 꽂혀 있는 것을 발견했습니다. 번역본은 영어원서만큼 감동을 주지 못하고 애매하게 해석된 부분도 많았습니다. 그래서 50대 후반의 나이에 원서로 꼼꼼히 한 줄 한 줄 음미하면서 그 책을 다시 읽었습니다. 그리고 『데미안』의 끝 부분, 전쟁 중 부상당한 데미안과 싱클레어의 해우, 데미안의 죽음에 이르는 대목에서 나도 모르게 흘러내리는 눈물을 억제할 수 없었습니다. 그것은 '아! 나도 이마에 카인의 흔적을 가진 두 주인공을 닮아 있구나!'라는 깨달음에서 오는 눈물이었습니다. 이 말의 의미가 무엇인지 여러분 스스로 이 책을 읽으면서 알아 가신다면, 여러분 삶에 많은 변화가 있을 것이고, 지금 어려움의 삶이 힘들고 고독하다면 그것을 극복하는 힘을 제공해 줄 것입니다.

이 책은 중급이상의 영어 수준을 지닌 독자가 읽을 것을 권장합니다. 어려운 구문들이 많아서 독해하기 매우 힘든 부분에 대해서는 문법과 구조 설명, 단어 해석, 문장 해석 등이 영어지문 바로 옆에 제공되어 있기 때문에 참고로 하면서 읽는다면 내용에 대한 이해뿐만 아니라 영어실력 향상에도 많은 도움이 될 것이라고 생각합니다. 이 책은 한 번 읽고 덮어 둘 그런 책은 아닙니다. 그래서 세 번 정도 읽기를 권장합니다. 그렇게 하면 읽을 때마다 다른 감동이 밀려올 것입니다.

DEMIAN

The Story of Emil Sinclair's Youth by Hermann Hesse[1]

I wanted only to try to live in accord with the promptings[2] which came from my true self. Why was that so very difficult?

---

1) Source: https://www.msjkeeler.com/uploads/1/4/0/6/1406968/demian.pdf
2) prompting: 대사 일러주기, promptings 나의 진정한 내면에서 울러 나오는 목소리

Prologue

I cannot tell my story without reaching a long way back. If it **were** possible I **would** reach back farther still—into the very first years of my childhood, and beyond them into distant ancestral past 먼 조상의 과거. Novelists **when** they write novels tend to take an almost godlike attitude toward their subject, **pretending** to a total comprehension 이해 of the story, a man's life, which they can therefore recount as God Himself might, nothing **standing** between them and the naked truth 적나라한 진실, the entire story **meaningful** in every detail. I am as little able to do this as the novelist is, even though my story is more important to me than any novelist's is to him—for 왜냐하면 this is my story; it is the story of a man, not of an invented, or possible, or idealized, or otherwise 달리 absent figure 공허한 인물, but of a unique being 독특한 인간 of flesh and blood. Yet, what a real living human being is made of seems to be less understood today than at any time before, and men—each one of **whom** represents 나타내다 a unique and valuable experiment on the part of nature — are therefore shot wholesale nowadays.

If we **were** not something more than unique human beings, if each one of us **could** really be done away with once and for all by a single bullet, storytelling **would** lose all purpose. But every man is more than just himself; he also represents the unique, the very special and always significant and remarkable point **at which** the world's phenomena intersect, only once in this way and never again. That is **why** every man's story is important, eternal, sacred 영원하고 신성한 ; that is **why** every man, **as long as** he lives and fulfills the will of nature, is

reaching=going

가정법 과거:
만약 ~하다면, ~ 것이다

분사구 pretending to
~하는 척 하면서

recount=explain in detail
nothing **standing** between
~사이에 아무것도 두지 않고
entire story **meaningful**:
전체 이야기에 의미를
부여하면서
as the novelist is (able to do)
any novelist's (story is important) to him

what a real ~ made of
'진정 살아있는 인간이란 무엇인가' 하는 것은

each one of whom
=and each one of the men
on the part of nature
자연의 입장에서는
therefore 그런 까닭에
be shot wholesale
대거 죽임을 당하다

가정법 과거

be done away with
완전히 제거되다
and for all 한 번에

remarkable point
주목할 만 한 점(존재)
at which=and at the point
그리고 그 점에서 세상의 현상들이 교차하다
관계부사 why=그것이 바로
~한 이유이다

접속사 as long as: ~하는 한

wondrous 불가사의한, and worthy of every consideration 주목. In each individual the spirit has become flesh, in each man the creation suffers, within each one a redeemer 구세주 is nailed to the cross.

within each ~ cross
각자의 내면에서 한 구세주가
십자가에 매달려 있다

Few people nowadays know what man is. Many sense this ignorance 무지 and die the more easily because of it, the same way **that** I will die more easily **once** I have completed this story. I do not consider myself less ignorant than most people. I have been and still am a seeker 구도자, but I have ceased to question stars and books; I have begun to listen to the teachings my blood whispers to me. My story is not a pleasant one; it is **neither** sweet **nor** harmonious, **as** invented stories are; it has the taste of nonsense and chaos 혼돈, of madness and dreams—like the lives of all men who stop deceiving themselves 자신을 속이다. Each man's life represents a road toward himself, an attempt at such a road, the intimation 암시 of a path. No man has ever been entirely and completely himself. Yet each one strives 노력하다 to become that—**one** in an awkward, **the other** in a more intelligent way, each as best he can. Each man carries the vestiges 흔적 of his birth—the slime 점액 and eggshells 알껍데기 of his primeval past 태고의 과거 —with him to the end of his days. Some never become human, **remaining** frog, lizard, ant. Some are human above the waist, fish below. Each represents a gamble 모험 on the part of nature in creation of the human. We all share the same origin, our mothers; all of us come in at the same door.

sense=feel

the same way that:
~와 똑 같은 방식으로
접속사 once: 일단 ~하면

cease to ~ books
점성술을 믿거나 책에
의존하지 아니 한다.
listen ~ to me
나의 피가 나에게 속삭이는
가르침에 귀를 기울인다.

neither A nor B:
A도 B도 아니다
접속사 as: ~하듯
have the taste of
~의 느낌을 주다
each man's ~ himself
각자의 삶은 자기 자신에게로
이르는 길이다.

one in ~, the other in ~
하나는 ~, 다른 하나는 ~한
방식으로
as best he can
=as best as possible

분사구 remaining:
~상태로 남아 있으면서

But each of us—experiments of the depths— strives toward his own destiny 운명. We can understand one another; but each of us is able to interpret 설명하다 himself to himself alone.

experiments of the depths
심연으로부터 나온
시도/시험/모험

each of us ~ alone
결국 자신을 가장 잘 아는
것은 자신뿐이다.

Chapter I
Two Realms

Source: https://pixabay.com/illustrations/good-and-evil-angels-and-demons-4983193/

I. Two Realms

realm=world 영역, 세계

I shall begin my story with an experience I had when I was ten and attended our small town's Latin school.

The sweetness of many things from that time still stirs 흥분시킨다 and touches me with melancholy 우울: dark and well-lighted alleys 오솔길, houses and towers, chimes 종소리 and faces, **rooms rich** and comfortable, warm and relaxed, **rooms pregnant** with secrets 비밀을 잉태한. Everything bears 가지다 the scent of warm intimacy 친밀, servant girls, household remedies 비상약, and dried fruits.

관/대+be동사 생략구조:
=the rooms (which were) rich
=the rooms (which were) pregnant

The realms of day and night, two different worlds coming from two opposite poles 반대의 극, mingled 뒤섞이다 during this time. My parents' house made up one realm, yet its boundaries 경계 were even narrower, actually **embracing** only my parents themselves. This realm was familiar to me in almost every way — mother and father, love and strictness 엄격함, model behavior, and school. It was a realm of brilliance 광휘, clarity 명료, and cleanliness, gentle conversations, washed hands, clean clothes, and good manners. This was the world **in which** morning hymns 찬송가 were sung and Christmas celebrated. Straight lines and paths led into the future: there were duty and guilt, bad conscience 양심 and confession 고해, forgiveness 용서 and good resolutions 결심, love, reverence 숭배, wisdom and the words of the Bible. If one wanted an unsullied 훼손되지 않은 and orderly 올바른 life, one made sure one was in league with this world.

현재분사 embracing:
=and they embraced

in which=where

Christmas (was) celebrated

be in league with
~와 동맹/결탁하다

The other realm, however, **overlapping** half our house, was completely different; it smelled different, spoke a different language, promised and demanded different things. This second world contained 포함하다 servant girls and workmen, ghost stories, rumors of scandal. It was

분사구 overlapping:
~와 절반이 겹치는

dominated by a loud mixture of horrendous 무서운, intriguing 호기심을 자아내는, frightful 놀라운, mysterious things, including slaughterhouses 도살장 and prisons, drunkards and screeching 소리를 지르는 fishwives, calving cows 송아지를 낳는 암소, horses sinking to their death 죽어가는, tales of robberies 강도, murders 살인자, and suicides 자살. All these wild and cruel, attractive and hideous 섬뜩한 things surrounded us, could be found in the next alley, the next house. Policemen and tramps 쿵쿵거리는 소리, drunkards who beat their wives, droves 인파 of young girls **pouring** out of factories at night, old women who put the hex on you **so that** you fell ill, thieves **hiding** in the forest, arsonists **nabbed** by country police — everywhere this second vigorous 활발한 world erupted 분출하다 and gave off 발산하다 its scent, everywhere, that is, except 제외하고 in our parents' rooms. And that was good. It was wonderful **that** peace and orderliness, quiet and a good conscience, forgiveness and love, ruled in this one realm, and **it** was wonderful **that** the rest existed, too, the multitude of harsh noises 수많은 거친 소음, of sullenness 우울 and violence 폭력, **from which** one could still escape with a leap 도약 into one's mother's lap 무릎.

It was strange how both realms bordered on each other, how close together they were! For example, when Lina, our servant girl, sat with us by the living-room door at evening prayers 기도 and added 더하다 her clear voice to the hymn, her washed hands **folded** on her smoothed-down apron 깔끔하게 다림질한 앞치마, she belonged with father and mother, to us, to those **that** dwelled 살다 in light and righteousness 정의. But afterwards, in the kitchen or woodshed 목재 헛간, when she told me the story of "the tiny man with no head," or when she argued with neighborhood women in the butcher shop 고깃간, she was

be dominated by
~의 지배를 받다

분사 pouring out of
~에서 쏟아져 나오는
put the hex on ~
~에게 마법을 걸다
so that: ~하기 위해서
분사 hiding 숨어있는 도둑
분사 nabbed 체포된 방화범

가주어 it, 진주어 that 2개

from which:
그러한 것들로부터

간접의문문 순서:
how both realms bordered
how close ~ they were

(with)+목적어+분사구:
=(with) her washed hands
folded on 그녀의 씻은 손을
포개어 ~에 놓고
관계대명사 that:
=that(=who) dwelled in

someone else, belonged to another world **which** veiled her with mystery. And that's how it was with everything, most of all with myself. Unquestionably 의심할 여지없이 I belonged to the realm of light and righteousness; I was my parents' child. But in **whichever** direction I turned I perceived 지각하다 the other world, and I lived within that other world as well 또한, **though** often a stranger to it, and suffering from panic and a bad conscience. There were times **when** I actually preferred 더 좋아하다 living in the forbidden realm 금지된 영역, and frequently 자주, returning to the realm of light — necessary and good as it may have been — seemed almost like returning to something less beautiful, something rather drab 단조로운 and tedious 지루한. Sometimes I was absolutely certain that my destiny was to become like mother and father, **as** clear-sighted 명민한 and unspoiled, **as** orderly and superior **as** they. But this goal seemed far away and to reach it meant attending endless schools, studying, passing tests and examinations, and this way led past and through the other, darker realm. **It** was not at all impossible **that** one might remain a part of it and sink into it. There were stories of sons who had gone astray 타락하다, stories I read with passion. These stories always pictured the homecoming as such a relief 구원 and as something **so** extraordinary 특별한 **that** I felt convinced 확신하다 that this alone was the right, the best, the sought-for thing. Still, the part of the story **set** among the evil and the lost was more appealing 흥미를 끄는 by far, and — if I **could have admitted** it — at times 때때로 I didn't want the Prodigal Son 돌아온 탕아 to repent 회개하다 and be found again. But one didn't dare think this, much less say it out loud. It was only present 존재하는 somehow as a premonition 예감/전조, a possibility at the

---

관계대명사 which:
~로 얼굴을 가린
만사가 다 그러했고,
나 자신은 더욱 그러했다.

복합관계형용사 in whichever:
어느 방향으로 몸을 돌려도

(주어+be) 생략구조:
=though (I was) often a stranger to it

관계부사 when:
~하던 때가 있었다.

동명사 주어 returning

(관/대+be) 생략구조:
=something (which was) less beautiful

as B1, as B2 as A:
A만큼 B한

lead past ~를 지나가다

가주어 it, 진주어 that
어두운 세계의 일부가 되어 그 속에 가라앉는 일

stories of sons 성경에 나오는 탕아의 이야기

picture A as B
A를 B로 묘사하다
so A(형) that B(문장)
너무 A해서 B하다
sought-for thing
추구해야 할 것
관계대명사 생략구조
=the story (which was) set among 악당과 탕아들이 나오는 이야기의 일부
가정법과거완료:
그것을 인정했다할지라도
dare 감히 ~하다

much less: 하물며(더욱더)
~이 아니다.

- 12 -

root of one's consciousness 의식. When I pictured the devil to myself I could easily imagine him on the street below, disguised 위장하다 or undisguised, or at the country fair or in a bar, but never at home with us.

My sisters, too, belonged to the realm of light. It often seemed to me that they had a greater natural affinity to my father and mother; they were better, better mannered, had fewer faults 결점 than I. They had their faults, of course; they had their bad moments, but these did not appear to go very deep 심각하다 as they did with me, **whose** contact with evil often grew so oppressive 가혹한 and painful, and **to whom** the dark world seemed so much closer. Sisters, like parents, were to be comforted and respected; if I had quarreled with them I always reproached 비난하다 myself afterwards, felt like the instigator 선동자, the one who had to ask for forgiveness. **For** by offending 화나게 하다 my sisters I offended my parents, all **that** was good and superior. There were secrets I would far rather 훨씬 더 많이 have shared with the lowest hoodlum 건달/깡패 than with my sisters. On good days, when my conscience did not trouble me, it was often delightful to play with them, to be good and decent 예의바른 as they were and to see myself in a noble light. That's **what** it must have been like to be an angel! It was the highest state 상태 one could think of.

But how infrequent 드문 such days were! Often at play, at some harmless activity, I became **so** fervent 격렬한 and headstrong 고집스런 **that** I was too much 과한 for my sisters; the quarrels and unhappiness this led to threw me into **such** a rage **that** I became horrible, did and said things **so** awful they seared 태우다 my heart even as I said them. Then followed harsh 가혹한 hours of gloomy regret and contrition 회개, the painful moment when I begged

at the root of
~의 깊숙한 곳에

have an affinity to
~와 본질적 유사성을 가지다

these=bad moments

they=bad moments
소유격관계대명사:
whose contact with devil
=but my contact with evil
to whom=and to me
were to=should

접속사 for: 왜냐하면

관계대명사 that:
선하고 우수한 모든 것

That's what ~ angel!
천사가 된다는 것이 그와
같이 행동하는 것이었음에
틀림없었다.

so ~ that 구조: 너무 ~해서

목적격 관/대 which 생략:
=the quarrels and
unhappiness (which) this
led to 이러한 행동의 결과로
생긴 언쟁과 불행은
so awful (that) I become ~

forgiveness, to be followed again by beams of light, a quiet, thankful, undivided gladness.

I attended the Latin school. The mayor's son and the head forester's 산림감독관의 son were in my class; both visited me at home at times, and though they were quite unruly 제멋대로 구는, they were both members of the good, the legal world. Yet this did not mean that I had no dealings with some of the neighborhood boys who attended public school and **on whom** we usually looked down. It is with one of them that I must begin my story.

One half-holiday — I was little more than ten years old — two neighborhood kids and I were roaming about when a much bigger boy, a strong and burly 덩치가 큰 kid from public school, the tailor's son, joined us. His father drank and the whole family had a bad name. I had heard much about **Franz Kromer**, was afraid of him, didn't at all like that he came up to us. His manners were already those of a man and he imitated 흉내 내다 the walk and speech of young factory workers. Under his leadership we clambered down the riverbank by the bridge and hid below the first arch. The narrow strip between the vaulted wall of the bridge 아치형 교각 and the lazily 천천히 flowing river was covered with nothing but refuse 쓰레기, shards 파편, tangled bundles of rusty wire and other rubbish 잡동사니. Occasionally 때때로 one could pick up something useful here. Franz Kromer instructed 가르치다 us to comb the area and show him **what** we found. He would **either** pocket it **or** fling 던져버리다 it into the river. He put us on the lookout for objects made of lead 납, brass 황동, and tin 주석, all of which he tucked away — also an old comb made of horn. I felt very uneasy in his presence, **not only** because I knew that my father would not have approved of my being seen in his company, **but** because I was simply afraid of Franz himself, though I was glad that he seemed to accept me and treat me like the others. He gave instructions 지시 and we obeyed 복종하다 — it seemed like an old habit, even though this was the first time I was with him.

After a while we sat down. Franz spit 침을 뱉다 into the water, and he looked like a man; he spit through a gap between his teeth and hit **whatever** he aimed at. A conversation started up, and the boys began boasting 자랑하다 and heaping praise on themselves for all sorts of schoolboy heroics 영웅적 행동 and tricks 장난 they had played. I kept quiet and yet was afraid I'd be noticed 알아채다, that my silence might particularly incur 초래하다 Kromer's wrath 분노. My two friends had begun to shun 피하다 me the very moment Franz Kromer had joined us. I was a stranger among them and felt that my manners and clothes presented a kind of challenge 도전. As a Latin school boy, the spoiled son of a well-to-do 부유한 father, it would be impossible for Franz to like me, and the other two, I felt acutely 예민하게, would soon disown and desert 버리다 me.

Finally, out of sheer nervousness, I began telling a story too. I invented 지어내다 a long tale about a robbery 도둑질 **in which** I filled the role of hero. In a garden near the mill, I said, together with a friend, I had stolen a whole sackful of 한 자루의 apples one night, and by no means ordinary apples, but apples of the very best sort. **It was** the fear of the moment **that** made me seek refuge 도피처 in this story — inventing and telling stories came naturally to me. In order not to fall immediately 즉시 silent again, and perhaps become involved in something worse, I gave a complete display of my narrative powers. One of us, I continued, had had to stand guard 망을 보다

복합관계대명사 whatever
=no matter what 그가 목표로 하는 것은 무엇이든지
heaping praise
~에 대해서 자신들에 대한 칭찬을 쌓아가다

disown ~와 관계가 없다고 말하다

out of sheer nervousness 순전한 불안감에서

관계부사 in which=where 그 이야기에서 나를 주인공으로 만들었다.

by no means 결코~가 아니다

강조구문 It was A that B: B 한 것은 A였다
순간의 두려움을 피하기 위해 이야기를 꾸며내어 도피처로 삼았다.

(not to) become involved in 더 나쁜 일에 말려들지 않기 위해서

while the other climbed the tree and shook out the apples. Moreover, the sack had grown **so** heavy **that** we had to open it again, **leaving** half the apples behind. But half an hour later we had returned and fetched 가져오다 the rest.

When I had finished I waited for approval 승인 of some sort. I had warmed to my subject toward the end and been carried away by my own eloquence. The two younger ones kept silent, waiting, but Franz Kromer looked sharply at me out of narrowed eyes 실눈으로 and asked threateningly 위협적으로:

"Is that true?"

"Yes," I said.

"Really and truly?"

"Yes, really and truly," I insisted stubbornly 고집스럽게 **while choking** 숨 막히는 inwardly with fear.

"Would you swear 맹세하다 to it?"

I became very afraid but at once said yes.

"Then say: By God and the grace of my soul."

"By God and the grace of my soul," I said.

"Well, all right," he said and turned away.

I thought everything was all right now, and was glad when he got up and turned to go home. After we had climbed back up to the bridge, I said hesitantly 주저하며 that I would have to head for home myself.

"You can't be in that much of a hurry." Franz laughed. "We're going in the same direction 방향, aren't we?"

Slowly he ambled on and I didn't dare run off; he was in fact walking in the direction of my house. When we stood in front of it and I saw the front door and the big brass knocker 놋쇠 손잡이, the sun in the windows and the curtain in my mother's room, I breathed a sigh of relief.

When I quickly opened the door and slipped in,

분사구 leaving:
=and left half the apples ~

I had warmed ~ eloquence
내가 지어낸 이야기에 열이 오르고 나의 달변에 스스로 심취했다.

while (주어+be) 생략구조:
=while (I was) choking
속으로는 겁이 나서 숨이 막힐 것 같은데도

amble on 느릿느릿 걷다

breathe a sigh of relief
안도의 한숨을 쉬다

reaching to slam it shut, Franz Kromer edged in 틈새로 밀고 들어오다 behind me. In the cool tiled passageway, **lit** only by one window **facing** the courtyard, he stood beside me, held on to me and said softly:

"Don't be in such a rush, you."

I looked at him, **terrified** 겁에 질려. His grip on my arm was like a vise 죔틀. I wondered *what he might have* in mind and **whether** he wanted to hurt me. I tried to decide whether if I screamed now, screamed loud and piercingly 날카롭게, someone could come down from above quickly enough to save me. But I gave up the idea.

"What is it?" I asked. "What do you want?"

"Nothing much. I only wanted to ask you something. The others don't have to hear it."

"Oh, really? I can't think of anything to say to you. I have to go up, you know."

Softly Franz Kromer asked: "You know who owns the orchard 과수원 by the mill, don't you?"

"I'm not sure. The miller, I think."

Franz had put his arm around me and now he drew me **so** close I was forced to look into his face inches away 바로 코앞에서. His eyes were evil, he smiled maliciously 악의적으로; his face was filled with cruelty 잔인함 and a sense of power.

"Well, I can tell you for certain whose orchard that is. I've known for some time **that** someone had stolen apples there and **that** the man **who** owns it said he'd give two marks to anyone **who**'d tell him who swiped them."

"Oh, my God!" I exclaimed. "You wouldn't do that, would you?"

I felt it would be useless to appeal to his sense of honor. He came from the other world: betrayal 배신 was

분사구 reaching:
문을 닫으려고 손을 뻗자
분사구 lit, facing:
마당과 마주한 창에서 나오는
빛으로 밝혀진 통로

간접의문문: 의문사+주+동
접속사 whether (목적):
~인지 아닌지

don't have to=need not
~할 필요가 없다

so ~ (that) 생략구조:
so close (that) I was ~

간접의문문: 의문사+주+동
whose orchard that is
know that ~을 알고 있었다

주격관계대명사 who:
~하는 사람
swipe=steal

no crime to him. I sensed this acutely 정확하게. The people from the other world were not like us in these matters.

"Not say anything?" laughed Kromer. "Kid, what do you take me for? Do you think I own a mint? I'm poor, I don't have a wealthy father like you and if I can earn two marks I earn them any way I can. Maybe he'll even give me more."

Suddenly he let go of me. The passageway no longer smelled of peace and safety, the world around me began to crumble 무너지다. He would give me away to the police! I was a criminal 범죄자; my father would be informed — perhaps even the police would come. All the dread 공포 of chaos threatened 위협하다 me, everything ugly and dangerous was united against me. It meant nothing **that** I'd filched 훔치다 nothing. I'd sworn 맹세하다 I had!

Tears welled up 샘솟다 in my eyes. I felt I had to strike a bargain and desperately 필사적으로 I groped through all my pockets. Not a single apple, no pocket knife, I had nothing at all. I thought of my watch, an old silver watch **that** didn't work, **that** I wore just for the fun of it. It had been my grandmother's. Quickly I took it off 풀다.

I said: "Kromer, listen! Don't give me away. It wouldn't be fair if you did. I'll give you my watch **as** a present, here, take a look. **Otherwise** 그 외에 I've nothing at all. You can have it, it's made of silver, and the works, well, there's something slightly wrong with them; you have to have it fixed."

He smiled and weighed the watch in his palm. I looked at his hand and felt how brutal and deeply hostile 적대적인 it was to me, how it reached for my life and peace.

"It's made of silver," I said hesitantly.

"I don't give a damn for your silver and your old watch," he said scornfully. "*Get it fixed* yourself."

in these matters
이런 일에 있어서

what do you ~ for? 너는
나를 무엇으로 생각하니?
mint=big money

mark: 독일의 화폐단위

give me away to
나를 ~에게 넘기다
be informed=know it

be united against me
나에게 맞서기 위해 뭉치다
가주어 it, 진주어 that
swear-swore-sworn

strike a bargain
흥정을 하다
grope through
샅샅이 뒤지다

주격 관계대명사 that
wear-wore-worn 차다, 입다

give A away to B:
A를 B에게 넘기다

전치사 as: 선물로

사역동사+목+목적보어(pp):
have it fixed 수리해야한다

give a damn for=have
interest in 관심을 가지다
사역동사+목+목/보(pp)
get it fixed

"But, Franz!" I exclaimed, **trembling** with fear **that** he might run away. "Wait, wait a moment. Why don't you take it? It's really made of silver, honest. And I don't have anything else."

He threw me a cold scornful 경멸하는 look.

"Well, you know who I'll go to. Or I could go to the police too. . . I'm on good terms with the sergeant 경찰관."

He turned **as if** to go. I held on to his sleeve 소매를 붙잡다. I couldn't allow him to go. I would rather have died than suffer **what** might happen if he went off like that.

"Franz," I implored 간청하다, **hoarse** with excitement,

"don't do anything foolish. You're only joking, aren't you?"

"Yes, I'm joking, but it could turn into an expensive joke."

"Just tell me what I'm supposed to do, Franz. I'll do anything you ask."

He looked me up and down with narrowed eyes and laughed again.

"Don't be so stupid," he said with false good humor. "You know as well as I that I'm in a position to earn two marks. I'm not a rich man **who** can afford to throw them away, but you're rich — you even have a watch. **All** you have to do is give me two marks; then everything will be all right."

I understood his logic 논리. But two marks! That was **as** much and **as** unattainable **as** ten, **as** a hundred, **as** a thousand. I didn't have a pfennig. There was a piggy bank that my mother kept for me. When relatives came to visit they would drop in five- or ten-pfennig pieces. That was **all** I had. I had no allowance 용돈 at that time.

"I just don't have any," I said sadly. "I don't have any

분사구 trembling:
두려움으로 떨면서
동격의 that: 그가 휙 가버릴 지도 모른 다는 두려움

be on good terms with
~와 사이가 좋다
접속사 as if:
마치 ~할 것처럼
would rather A than B:
B하느니 A하는 게 더 낫다
관계대명사 what: ~하게 되면 발생할 모든 것을 겪느니보다

(being) 생략 분사구:
(being) hoarse with
흥분해서 목쉰 소리로

turn into ~로 변하다

as well as ~만큼 잘

주격 관계대명사 who:
afford to ~할 여유가 있다

목적격 관/대 that 생략:
All (that) you have to do

as ~ as: ~만큼 -한

pfennig 페니히: 독일의 동전 100분의 1 마르크

목적격 관/대 that 생략:
all (that) I had

money at all. But I'll give you **everything else** I have. I have a Western, tin soldiers, and a compass. Wait, I'll get them for you."

목적격 관/대 that 생략: everything else (that) I have

Kromer's mouth merely twisted into a brief sneer 냉소. Then he spit on the floor.

Harshly 가혹하게 he said: "You can keep your crap 쓰레기. A compass! Don't make me mad! You hear, I'm after money."

I'm after money! 난 돈을 노려(원해).

"But I don't have any, I never get any, I can't help it."

"All right, then you'll bring me the two marks tomorrow. I'll wait for you after school down near the market place. That's all. You'll see what'll happen if you don't bring it."

"But where am I going to get it if I don't have any?"

"There's plenty of money in your house. That's your business. Tomorrow after school. And I'm telling you: if you don't have it with you. . ." He threw me a withering 기를 죽이는 look, spit once more, and vanished 사라지다 like a shadow.

I couldn't even get upstairs. My life was wrecked 파괴되다. I thought of running away and never coming back, or of drowning myself. However 그러나, I couldn't picture any of this very clearly. In the dark, I sat down on the bottom step 맨 아래 칸 of our staircase, **huddled** up within myself, **abandoning** myself to misery. That's **where** Lina found me weeping **as** she came downstairs with the basket to fetch wood.

분사구 huddled up: 웅크리고 주저앉아
분사구 abandoning: 불행에 나 자신을 맡기고
관계부사 선행사 생략: (the place) where Lina ~
접속사 as = when

I begged her not to say a word, then I went upstairs. To the right of the glass door hung my father's hat and my mother's parasol; they gave me a feeling of home and comfort, and my heart greeted them thankfully, **as** the Prodigal Son 방탕아 might greet the sight and smell of old familiar rooms. But all of it was lost to me now, all

도치구조: 장소+동사+주어 hung (동) my father's ~ parasol (주) hang-hung-hung
접속사 as: ~하듯이

of it belonged to the clear, well-lighted world of my
father and mother, and I, **guilty and deeply engulfed** in
an alien world, was entangled in adventures and sin,
threatened by an enemy, — by dangers, fear, and shame.
The hat and parasol, the old sandstone 사암 **floor** I was
so fond of 좋아하다, the broad picture above the hall
cupboard, the voice of my elder sister coming to me
from the living room were all more moving 감동적인, more
precious, more delicious than ever before, but they had
ceased to be a refuge 피난처 and **something** I could rely
on; they had become an unmistakable reproach 명백한 치욕.
None of this was mine any more, I could no longer take
part in its quiet cheerfulness. My feet had become
muddied, I could not even wipe them clean on the mat;
everywhere I went I was followed by a darkness **of which**
this world of home knew nothing. How many secrets I
had had, how often I had been afraid — but all of it had
been child's play **compared** with what I brought home
with me today. I was haunted 시달리다 by misfortune, it
was reaching out toward me **so that** not even my mother
could protect me, **since** she was not even allowed to
know. **Whether** my crime was stealing or lying — (hadn't
I sworn a false oath 거짓 맹세 by God and everything that
was sacred? 신성한) — was immaterial. My sin was not
specifically 명확히 this or that but consisted of 구성되다
having shaken hands with the devil. Why had I gone
along? Why had I obeyed Kromer — better even than I
had ever obeyed my father? Why had I invented the
story, **building** myself up with a crime **as though** it were
a heroic act? The devil held me in his clutches 발톱, the
enemy was behind me.

For the time being 한동안 I was not so much afraid of
what would happen tomorrow as of the horrible certainty

분사 (being) 생략:
(being) guilty and (being)
deeply engulfed 죄의식을
느끼고 ~에 깊이 가라앉아
be entangled in ~에 얽혀
(being) threatened by
적으로부터 협박을 당하여
목적격 관/대 that 생략:
floor (that) I was fond of

목적격 관/대 that 생략
=something (that) I could
rely on 내가 기댈 수 있는 것

양보의 부사절 everywhere:
내가 어디를 가든
a darkness of which:
이 고향과 같은 세계는 알지
못하는 어둠이 뒤따르다

분사구 compared with:
~와 비교하면

결과 접속사 so that:
그래서 ~하다

접속사 since=because

immaterial
=not important

분사구 building:
도둑질 이야기를 스스로
꾸며대면서
as if/though 가정법
마치 ~인 것처럼

not so much A as B:
A가 아니라 B가 더 두렵다

that my way, from now on, would lead farther and farther downhill into darkness. I felt acutely **that** new offenses 범죄 were bound to grow out of his one offense, **that** my presence among my sisters, greeting and kissing my parents, were a lie, **that** I was living a lie concealed 숨겨진 deep inside myself.

For a moment, hope and confidence 확신 flickered up inside me **as** I gazed at my father's hat. I would tell him everything, would accept his verdict 판단 and his punishment, and would make him into my confessor 고해신부 and savior 구세주. It would only be a penance 참회, **the kind** I had often done, a bitterly difficult hour, a ruefully 가엾게도 difficult request for forgiveness.

How sweet and tempting 솔깃한 that sounded! But it was no use. I knew I wouldn't do it. I knew I now had a secret, a sin **which** I would have to expiate 속죄하다 alone. Perhaps I stood at the parting of the ways, perhaps I would now belong among the wicked forever, share their secrets, depend on them, obey them, have to become one of their kind. I had acted the man and hero, now I had to bear 견디다 the consequences 결과.

I was glad when my father took me to task for my muddy boots. It diverted 전환하다 his attention by sidestepping 회피하다 the real issue and placed me in a position to endure reproaches 질책 **that** I could secretly transfer to the other, the more serious offense. A strange new feeling overcame me at this point, a feeling that stung pleasurably: I felt superior to my father! Momentarily 일시적으로 I felt a certain loathing 혐오 for his ignorance 무지. His upbraiding 책망 me for muddy boots seemed pitiful. "If you only knew" crossed my mind as I stood there like a criminal **being** cross-examined for a stolen loaf of bread when the actual crime was murder.

접속사 that (목적): 3개
~를 확실히 느끼다
be bound to ~
반드시 ~하게 되어 있다

(관/대+ be) 생략구조:
a lie (which was)
concealed inside myself

flicker 깜빡이다

접속사 as=when

목적격 관계대명사 생략
=the kind (that) I have
often done ~한 종류의

목적격 관/대 which

나는 인생의 기로/갈림길에
서 있는지도 모른다.
the wicked 사악한 사람들

어른 행세를 하고 영웅놀이를
했다.

take A to task for B:
B에 대해서 A를 책망하다
It 구두가 젖은 것

관계대명사 that:
다른, 좀 더 심각한 범죄에
전가할 수도 있었던 질책들을
나는 견딜 수 있었다.

sting-stung-stung 찌르다
superior to ~보다 우수한

cross one's mind
~한 생각이 마음에 떠오르다
being cross-examined for
~에 대해 추궁을 당하면서

It was an odious 가증스러운, hostile feeling, but it was strong and deeply attractive, and shackled 구속하다 me more than anything else to my secret and my guilt. I thought Kromer might have gone to the police by now and denounced 고발하다 me, that thunderstorms 폭풍우 were forming above my head, while all this time they continued to treat me like a little child.

This moment was the most significant 중대한 and lasting 영원한 of the whole experience. It was the first rent 틈 in the holy image of my father, it was the first fissure 균열 in the columns 기둥 that had upheld 지지하다 my childhood, **which** every individual must destroy before he can become himself. The inner, the essential line of our fate consists of such invisible experiences. Such fissures and rents grow together again, heal 아물다 and are forgotten, but in the most secret recesses 깊숙한 곳 they continue to live and bleed.

계속적용법 관/대 **which**
=and every individual must destroy the fissure

I immediately 즉시 felt **such** dread of this new feeling **that** I could have fallen down before my father and kissed his feet to ask forgiveness. But one cannot apologize for something fundamental 본질적인, and a child feels and knows this as well and as deeply as any sage.

such ~ that

sage=wise man

I felt the need to give some thought to my new situation, to reflect about what I would do tomorrow. But I did not find the time. All evening I was busy getting used to the changed atmosphere in our living room. Wall clock and table, Bible and mirror, bookcase and pictures on the wall were leaving me behind; I was forced to observe 관찰하다 with a chill in my heart 얼어붙은 마음으로 how my world, my good, happy, carefree life, was becoming a part of the past, was breaking away from me, and I was forced to feel how I was being shackled and held fast with new roots to the outside, to the dark and alien

be busy ~ing
~하느라 바쁘다
get/be used to ~ing/명사 :
~에 익숙해지다

leave me behind
나에게 이별을 고하다

break away from me
나에게서 떨어져 나가다
be shackled and held fast
단단히 구속되고 속박당하다

이질적인 world. For the first time in my life I tasted death, and death tasted bitter, for death is birth, is fear and dread of some terrible renewal 부활. I was glad when I finally lay in my bed. Just before, as my last torment 고통, I had had to endure evening prayers. We had sung a hymn **which** was one of my favorites. I felt unable to join in and every note galled me. When my father intoned the blessing — when he finished with "God be with us!" — something broke inside me and I was rejected 거절당하다 forever from this intimate 친밀한 circle. God's grace was with all of them, but it was no longer with me. Cold and deeply exhausted 녹초가 된, I had left them.

When I had lain in bed awhile, **enveloped** by its warmth and safety, my fearful heart turned back once more in confusion and hovered anxiously above **what** was now past. My mother had said good night to me as always. I could still hear her steps resound 울려 퍼지다 in the other room; the candle glow still illuminated the chink in the door. Now, I thought, now she'll come back once more, she has sensed something, she will give me a kiss and ask, ask kindly with a promise in her voice, and then I'll weep, then the lump in my throat will melt, then I will throw my arms around her, and then all will be well; I will be saved! And even after the chink in the door had gone dark I continued to listen and was certain **that** it simply would have to happen.

Then I returned to my difficulties and looked my enemy in the eye. I could see him clearly, one eye screwed up 찡그리다, his mouth twisted 일그러지다 into a brutal smile, and while I eyed him, **becoming** more and more convinced of the inevitable, he grew bigger and uglier and his evil eye lit up with a fiendish glint. He

lie-lay-lain 눕다

주격 관/대 which

gall ~를 불쾌하게 하다

intone 낮은 소리로 말하다

분사구 enveloped:
따뜻함과 온기에 둘러싸여

hovered anxiously above
걱정스럽게 ~주위를 맴돌다
what 관/대: 이제 과거가
되어버린 것
지각동사+목+동/원:
hear ~ resound
illuminate the chink
문틈을 비추다

lump in my throat
목구멍 속의 덩어리

접속사 that: ~를 확신하다

분사구 becoming:
점점 더 ~를 확신하면서
the inevitable(형):
피할 수 없는 것들

fiendish glint 사악한 번쩍임

was right next to me until I fell asleep, yet I didn't dream of him nor of what had happened that day. I dreamed instead that my parents, my sisters, and I were drifting 표류하다 in a boat, **surrounded** by absolute peace and the glow of a holiday. In the middle of the night I woke with the aftertaste 여운 of this happiness. I could still see my sisters' white summer dresses shimmer 살랑거리다 in the sun as I fell out of paradise back into reality, again face to face with the enemy, with his evil eye.

Next morning, when my mother came rushing up **shouting that** it was late and why was I still in bed, I looked sick. When she asked me **whether** anything was wrong, I vomited 토하다.

This seemed to be something gained 이득을 본 것. I loved being slightly sick, **being allowed** to lie in bed all morning, **drinking** camomile tea, **listening to** my mother tidy up the other rooms or Lina deal with the butcher in the hallway. Mornings off from school seemed enchanted, like a fairy tale; the sun playing in the room was not the same sun **shut** out of school when the green shades 커튼 were lowered. Yet even this gave me no pleasure today; there was something false about it.

If only I could die! But, as often before, I was only slightly unwell 아픈 and it was of no help, my illness protected me from school but not from Franz Kromer who would be waiting for me at eleven in the market place. And my mother's friendliness, instead of comforting me, was a distressing nuisance. I made a show of having fallen asleep again in order to be left alone to think. But I could see no way out. At eleven I had to be at the market. At ten I quietly got dressed and said that I felt better. The answer, as usual under these

not/neither A nor B:
A도 B도 하지 않았다

분사구 surrounded by:
~에 둘러싸여

지각동사+목+동/원:
see ~ shimmer

분사구 shouting that:
~하고 외치면서
간접의문문: 의문사+주+동:
문법 오류→ why I was still

분사구 병렬구조 3개:
하락 받아, 마시며, 들으며
지각동사+목+동/원, 2개
listening to A tidy up
or A deal with
enchanted=attractive

(관/대+be동사) 생략구조
=sun (which was) shut out
of school
녹색 커튼이 드리웠을 때
(교실에서) 눈부심을 막아주던
그런 태양은 아니었다.
false 거짓된, 가장된

distressing nuisance
괴로운 골칫거리

circumstances, was: either I went straight back to bed or in the afternoon I would have to be in school. I said I would gladly go to school. I had come up with a plan.

I couldn't meet Kromer penniless 한 푼도 없이. I had to get hold of my piggy bank. I knew it didn't contain enough, by no means enough, yet it was something, and I sensed that something was better than nothing, and that Kromer could at least be appeased.

In stocking feet I crept guiltily 죄책감을 느끼며 into my mother's room and took the piggy bank out of her desk; yet that was not half as bad as what had happened the day before with Kromer. My heart beat **so** rapidly **I felt** I would choke 질식하다. It did not ease up when I discovered downstairs that the bank was locked. Forcing it was easy, it was merely a matter of tearing the thin tin-plate grid 얇은 양철로 된 판; yet breaking it hurt 마음이 아프다 ― only now had I really committed a theft. Until then I had filched 훔치다 lumps of sugar or some fruit; this was more serious stealing, **even though** it was my own money I stole. I sensed how I was one step nearer Kromer and his world, how bit by bit everything was going downhill with me. I began to feel stubborn 완강한; let the devil take the hindmost! There was no turning back now. Nervously I counted the money. In the piggy bank it had sounded like so much more, but there was painfully little **lying** in my hand: sixty-five pfennigs. I hid the box on the ground floor, held the money clasped 꽉 쥐다 in my fist, and stepped out of the house, **feeling** more different than I had ever felt before when I walked through the gate. I thought I heard someone calling after me from upstairs but I walked away quickly.

There was still a lot of time **left**. By a very devious 꾸불꾸불한 route, I sneaked through the little alleys of a

come up with a plan
계획을 세우다

by no means=never
충분한 돈은 아니지만 그래도
조금은 있었다.

be appeased 달래지다

어제 있었던 일에 비하면
절반도 나쁘지 않았다.
so ~ (that) 생략구조:
so rapidly (that) I felt ~

commit a theft
도둑질을 하다
filch=steal
양보의 부사절 even though:
비록~일지라도

bit by bit=gradually

사역동사(let)+목+동/원:
let ~ take
the hindmost
가장 최후의 것

(주격 관/대+be동사) 생략
=little (which was) lying

분사구 feeling: 느끼면서

지각동사+목+-ing:
heard ~ calling

(주격 관/대+be동사) 생략
=time (which was) left
sneak through
몰래 빠져나오다

- 26 -

changed town, under a cloudy sky such as I had never seen before, past staring houses and people who eyed me with suspicion 의심. Then **it** occurred to me **that** a friend from school had once found a thaler in the cattle market. I would gladly have gone down on my knees and prayed that God perform a miracle and let me make a similar find. But I had forfeited 상실하다 the right to pray. And in any case, mending the box would have required a second miracle.

Franz Kromer spotted 발견하다 me from a distance, yet he approached me without haste and seemed to ignore me. When he was close, he motioned authoritatively for me to follow him, and without once turning back he walked calmly down the Strohgasse and across the little footbridge until he stopped in front of a new building at the outskirts 변두리. There were no workmen about, the walls were bare 휑한, doors and windows were blanks. Kromer took a look around, then walked through the entrance into the house and I followed him. He stepped behind a wall, gave me a signal, and stretched out his hand.

"Have you got it?" he asked coolly.

I drew my clenched fist 꽉 쥔 주먹 out of my pocket and emptied my money into his flat outstretched palm 펼친 손바닥. He had counted it even before the last pfennig piece had clinked down 쨍그랑 소리를 내다.

"That's sixty-five pfennigs," he said and looked at me.

"Yes," I said nervously. "That's all I have. I know it's not enough, but it's all I have."

"I thought you were cleverer than that," he scolded almost mildly. "Among men of honor you've got to do things right. I don't want to take anything away from you that isn't the right sum. You know that. Take your

---

past staring houses
마치 나를 응시하는 듯한 집들을 지나서
가주어 it, 진주어 that

thaler 탈러: 15~19세기에 독일에서 발행된 은화

사역동사(let)+목+동/원:
let ~ make
forfeited=lost
box=piggy bank
기적이 없는 한, 깨진 저금통이 원래대로 되지는 않을 것이다.

authoritatively 권위적으로

Strohgasse 슈트로 가세:
밀짚저장소가 있는 길
footbridge 인도

명예를 아는 남자들 사이에선 일이 공정하게 처리되어야 한다.
정확히 2마르크가 아니면 받지 않겠다.

pennies back, there! The other one — you know who — won't try to scale down the price. He pays up."

"But I simply don't have another pfennig. It's all I had in my bank."

"That's your business. But I don't want to make you unhappy. You owe me one mark, thirty-five pfennigs. When can I have them?"

"Oh, you'll get them for sure, Kromer. I just don't know when right now — perhaps I'll have more tomorrow or the day later. You understand, don't you, that I can't breathe 말하다 a word about this to my father."

"That's not my concern. I'm not out to do you any harm. I could have my money before lunch if I wanted, you know, and I'm poor. You wear expensive clothes and you're better fed than I. But I won't say anything. I can wait a bit. The day after tomorrow I'll whistle for you. You know what my whistle sounds like, don't you?"

He let me hear it. I had heard it before.

"Yes," I said, "I know it."

He left me **as though** he'd never seen me before. It had been a business transaction between the two of us, nothing more.

I think Kromer's whistle would frighten me even today if I suddenly heard it again. From now on I was to hear it repeatedly; it seemed to me I heard it all the time. There was not a single place, not a single game, no activity, no thought which this whistle did not penetrate, the whistle that made me his slave, **that** had become my fate. Frequently I would go into our small flower garden, **of which** I was so fond on those mild, colorful autumn afternoons, and an odd urge prompted 자극하다 me to play once more the childish games of my earlier years; I was playing, so to speak, the part of someone younger than

The other one ~ pays up.
다른 아이라면 (너처럼)
가격을 낮추지는 않을 거야.
그러면 전부 지불하겠지.

do A any harm:
A에게 어떤 해를 가하다

feed-fed-fed
be fed well 잘 먹다

사역동사(let)+목+동/원:
let ~ hear

as though=as if
마치 ~인 것처럼

was to=would 예정

penetrate 침투/관통 하다
관계대명사 that:
내 운명이 되어버린 이
휘파람 소리

be fond of ~를 좋아하다

myself, someone still good and free, innocent and safe. Yet into the midst of this haven 안식처 ― always **expected**, yet horribly surprising each time ― from somewhere Kromer's whistle would erupt 분출하다, **destroying** the game, **crushing** my illusions 환상. Then I would have to leave the garden to follow my tormentor 괴롭히는 자 to wicked, ugly places **where** I would have to give him an account 설명 of my pitiful finances 자금 and let myself be pressed for payment. The entire episode lasted perhaps several weeks, yet to me they seemed like years, an eternity 영원. Rarely did I have any money, at most 기껏해야 a five- or ten-pfennig piece **stolen** from the kitchen table when Lina had left the shopping basket lying around. Kromer upbraided 책망하다 me each time, **becoming** more and more contemptuous 경멸적인: I was cheating him, **depriving** him of what was rightfully his, I was stealing from him, **making** him miserable! Never in my life had I felt so distressed 곤궁에 처한, never had I felt more hopeless, more enslaved.

I had filled the piggy bank with play money and replaced it in my mother's desk. No one asked for it but the possibility **that** they might never left my thoughts. What frightened me even more than Kromer's brutal whistling was my mother's stepping up to me ― wasn't she coming to inquire about the piggy bank?

Because I had met my tormentor many times empty-handed, he began finding other means 수단 of torturing 괴롭히다 and using me. I had to work for him. He had to run various errands for his father; I had to do them for him. Or he would ask me to perform some difficult feat 묘기: hop for ten minutes on one leg, pin a scrap of paper on a passer-by's coat. Many nights in my dreams I elaborated on these tortures 고문 and lay

분사구 expected:
(휘파람소리는) 늘 예상하고 있었지만 그래도 매번 지독히도 나를 놀라게 한다
destroying, crushing 파괴하고 짓밟으면서

과거의 불규칙인 습관:
would ~하곤 했다

관계부사 where: ~한 곳으로

사역동사(let)+목+과/분:
let myself (be) pressed
빚 독촉을 당하다

부정부사(rarely) 도치구조
=I rarely had any money
(관/대+be동사) 생략구조
=piece (which was) stolen
lie-lying 놓여 있는

분사구 becoming:
그리고 점점 더 ~하다

deprive A of B:
A에게서 B를 빼앗다
부정부사(never) 도치구조
=In my life I had never ~
=I had never felt ~

동격의 that + 생략구조
=the possibility that they might (ask for it) / never left my thoughts

run errands
심부름을 가다

: 콜론 = 예를 들어

elaborate on
~에 대해 상세히 설명하다

drenched 흠뻑 젖은 in a nightmare's sweat.

For a while I actually became sick. I vomited 토하다 frequently and came down with frequent chills 한기, yet at night I would burn and sweat. My mother sensed that something was wrong and was very considerate 심각한, but this only tortured me the more **since** I could not respond by confiding in her.

One night, after I had gone to bed, she brought me a piece of chocolate. It reminded me of former years when, if I had been a good boy, I would receive such rewards 보상 before I fell asleep. Now she stood there and offered me the piece of chocolate. The sight was **so** painful **that** I could only shake my head. She asked me what was wrong and stroked my hair. All I could answer was: "No, no! I don't want anything." She placed the chocolate on my night table and left. The next morning, when she wanted to ask me about my behavior of the night before, I pretended 인체하다 to have forgotten the episode completely 완전히. Once 한번은 she brought the doctor, who examined me and prescribed 처방하다 cold baths in the morning.

My condition at that time was a kind of madness. Amid the ordered peace of our house I lived shyly, in agony 고뇌, like a ghost; I took no part in the life of the others, rarely forgot myself for an hour at a time. To my father, who was often irritated 짜증난 and asked me what was the matter, I was completely cold 냉담한.

꿈속에서도 크로머에 의해 고통을 계속 당했다.

접속사 since =as=because
confide in
~에게 속마음을 털어놓다

remind A of B:
A에게 B를 상기시키다

so ~ that 구조:
너무 ~해서 -하다

(I) rarely forgot ~ a time.
한 시간이나마 내 자신을 잊고 지낸 적이 드물었다.

Chapter II
Cain

Source: http://onlinecollection.nationalgallery.ie/objects/3123

2. Cain

My salvation 구원 came from a totally unexpected source 예상치 못한 곳, **which**, at the same time, brought a new element into my life that has affected 영향을 미치다 it to this very day.

A new boy had just been enrolled in 입학하다 our school. He was the son of a well-to-do widow who had come to live in our town; he wore a mourning band on his sleeve. Being several years older than I, he was assigned to a grade above me. Still, I could not avoid noticing him, nor could anyone else. This remarkable student seemed much older than he looked; in fact, he did not strike anyone as a boy at all. In contrast to us, he seemed strange and mature, like a man, or rather like a gentleman. He was not popular, did not take part in our games, still less in the general roughhouse 싸움질, and only his firm, self-confident tone toward the teachers won the admiration 칭찬 of the students. He was called Max Demian.

One day — as happened now and again — an additional 추가의 class was assigned to our large classroom for some reason or other. It was Demian's class. We, the younger ones, were having a Scripture 성경 lesson; the higher grade had to write an essay. While the story of Cain and Abel was being drummed into us, I kept glancing toward Demian **whose** face held a peculiar fascination 매력 for me, and I observed the intelligent, light, unusually resolute 결연한 face **bent** attentively 주의 깊게 and diligently over his work; he didn't at all look like a student **doing** an assignment 과제, but rather like a scientist **investigating** 조사하다 a problem of his own. I couldn't say that he made a favorable impression 좋은 인상

카인: 아담과 이브의 첫째 아들. 하나님 여호와가 동생 아벨의 제물은 받고 자기의 제물은 거절하자 분히 여겨 동생을 돌로 쳐서 죽인다.

관/대 계속적용법 which
=and it brought a new

well-to-do widow
부유한 미망인
mourning band
(죽음을) 애도하는 띠
be assigned to
~에 배정되다
avoid ~ing

부정어 도치구조:
=and anyone else could
nor avoid noticing him.

전혀 소년이라는 인상을 주지 않다

participate in 참석하다
=partake in, join
still less 하물며 ~는 더욱 하지 않다

now and again
= sometimes 이따금씩

be drummed into
~에게 주입되다
keep glancing
계속 쳐다보다
소유격 관/대 whose
=and his face held ~

(주격 관/대+be동사) 생략
=face (which was) bent
주의 깊게 숙인 얼굴
a student (who was) doing
a scientist (who was) investigating

on me; on the contrary 반대로, I had something against him: he seemed too superior and detached 초연한, his manner too provocatively confident, and his eyes gave him an adult expression — **which** children never like — faintly sad, with flashes of sarcasm 냉소. Yet I could not help looking at him, no matter whether I liked or detested 싫어하다 him, but if he happened to glance my way I averted 피하다 my eyes in panic. When I think back on it today, and what he looked like as a student at that time, I can only say that he was in every respect 모든 면에서 different from all the others, was entirely himself, with a personality 개성 all his own **which** made him noticeable 눈에 띄는 **even though** he did his best not to be noticed; his manner and bearing 행동거지 was that of a prince **disguised** among farm boys, **taking** great pains to appear one of them.

He was walking behind me on the way home from school, and after the others had turned off he caught up with me and said hello. Even his manner of greeting, though he tried to imitate our schoolboy tone, was distinctly 명백히 adult and polite.

"Shall we walk together for a while?" he asked. I felt flattered 우쭐한 and nodded. Then I described 설명하다 to him where I lived.

"Oh, over there?" he said and smiled. "I know the house. There's something odd 기묘한 above the doorway — it interested me at once."

I didn't know offhand 즉석에서 what he meant and was astonished 놀라다 that he apparently 명백히 knew our house better than I did myself. The keystone of the arch above the doorway bore no doubt a kind of coat of arms but it had worn off 닳다 with time and had frequently been painted over. As far as I knew it had nothing to do with us and our family.

"I don't know anything about it," I said shyly.

"It's a bird or something like that and must be quite old. The house is supposed to have been part of the monastery 수도원 at one point."

"That's quite possible." He nodded. "Take a good look at it sometime! Such things can be quite interesting. I believe it's a sparrow hawk."

We walked on. I felt very self-conscious. Suddenly Demian laughed as though something had struck him as funny.

"Yes, when we had class together," he burst out. "The story of Cain who has that mark on his forehead. Do you like it?"

No, I didn't. It was rare for me to like anything we had to learn. Yet I didn't dare confess 고백하다 it, for I felt I was being addressed by an adult. I said I didn't much mind the story.

Demian slapped me on the back.

"You don't have to put on an act for me. But in fact the story is quite remarkable 주목할 만한. It's far more remarkable than most stories we're taught in school. Your teacher didn't go into it at great lengths. He just mentioned the usual things about God and sin and so forth. But I believe —" He interrupted 중단하다 himself and asked with a smile: "Does this interest you at all?"

"Well, I think," he went on, "one can give this story about Cain quite a different interpretation 해석. Most of the things we're taught I'm sure are quite right and true, but one can view all of them from quite a different angle than the teachers do — and most of the time they then make better sense. For instance, one can't be quite satisfied with this Cain and the mark on his forehead,

have nothing to do with
~와 상관이 없다
must be ~임에 틀림없다

be supposed to
~한 것으로 추측되다

sparrow hawk 참새 매:
작은 새를 잡아먹는 매
self-conscious = abashed
수줍은, 겸연쩍은

burst out 불쑥 말하다

나는 어른과 이야기를 나누고
있다는 느낌이 들었다.
address ~에게 말을 걸다

put on an act
연기하다, 꾸며대다

go into it at great lengths
내용에 깊이 들어가다
and so forth 기타 등등

at all 조금이라도

'I'm sure' 삽입구

most of them ~ sense
우리가 배운 대부분의 것들을
더 나은 뜻을 가지게 된다.

forehead 이마의 표시/표식

- 34 -

with the way it's explained to us. Don't you agree? It's perfectly possible for someone to kill his brother with a stone and to panic and repent 후회하다. But that he's awarded a special decoration 표식 for his cowardice 비겁함, a mark that protects him and puts the fear of God into all the others, that's quite odd, isn't it?"

"Of course," I said with interest: the idea began to fascinate 매혹시키다 me. "But what other way of interpreting the story is there?"

He slapped me on the shoulder.

"It's quite simple! The first element of the story, its actual beginning, was the mark. Here was a man with something in his face that frightened the others. They didn't dare lay hands on him; he impressed them, he and his children. We can guess — no, we can be quite certain — that it was not a mark on his forehead like a postmark 우편소인— life is hardly ever as clear and straightforward 간단한 as that. It is much more likely **that** he struck people as faintly sinister 불길한, perhaps a little more intellect and boldness 대담 in his look than people were used to. This man was powerful: you would approach him only with awe 경외. He had a 'sign.' You could explain this any way you wished. And people always want what is agreeable to them and puts them in the right. They were afraid of Cain's children: they bore a 'sign.' So they did not interpret the sign for what it was — a mark of distinction 구별— but as its opposite. They said: 'Those fellows with the sign, they're a strange lot' 사람— and indeed they were. People with courage and character always seem sinister 불길한 to the rest. It was a scandal 사건 **that** a breed 종족 of fearless and sinister people ran about freely, so they attached a nickname and myth to these people to get even with them, to

---

with the way ~한 방식대로

decoration 훈장, 표식
cowardice 비겁함
카인의 이마의 표식은 카인을 보호해 줄뿐만 아니라 그 표식을 보는 사람들로 하여금 하느님에 대한 두려움을 느끼게 만든다.

But what other ~ is there?
그 이야기를 달리 해석할 방법이 있느냐?

lay hands on him
그에게 손을 대다, 건드리다

hardly ever 거의 ~아니다

he struck ~ sinister
사람들에게 어렴풋하지만 불길한 느낌을 주다

be agreeable to
~에게 맞는, 모순되지 않는
what puts them in the right 그들을 올바른 위치에 둘 수 있는 것
what it was 있는 그대로

It: 카인과 아벨의 이야기

동격의 that

get even with
~에게 복수/앙갚음하다

make up for the many times they had felt afraid — do you get it?"

"Yes — that is — in that case Cain wouldn't have been evil at all? And the whole story in the Bible is actually not authentic? 진짜의"

"Yes and no. Such age-old stories are always true but they aren't always properly recorded and aren't always given correct interpretations 해석. In short, I mean Cain was a fine fellow and this story was pinned on him only because people were afraid. The story was simply a rumor, something **that** people gab about, and it was true in so far as Cain and his children really bore a kind of mark and were different from most people."

I was astounded.

"And do you believe that the business about killing his brother isn't true either?" I asked, **entranced** 넋을 잃고.

"Oh, that's certainly true. The strong man slew a weaker one. It's doubtful whether it was really his brother, But it isn't important. Ultimately 궁극적으로 all men are brothers. So, a strong man slew a weaker one: perhaps it was a truly valiant act, perhaps it wasn't. At any rate 어쨌든, all the other weaker ones were afraid of him from then on 그때부터 계속, they complained bitterly 통렬히 and if you asked them: 'Why don't you turn around and slay him, too?' they did not reply 'Because we're cowards,' but rather 'You can't, he has a sign. God has marked him.' The fraud 사기 must have originated some way like that. — Oh well, I see I'm keeping you. So long then."

He turned into the Altgasse and left me standing there, more **baffled** than I had ever been in my life. Yet, almost as soon as he had gone, everything he had said seemed incredible 믿을 수 없는. Cain a noble person, Abel a coward!

Cain's mark a mark of distinction! It was absurd 터무니없는, it was blasphemous 불경한 and evil. How did God fit in 적합하다 in that case? Hadn't He accepted the sacrifice 제물 of Abel? Didn't He love Abel? No, what Demian had said was completely crazy. And I suspected 의심하다 that he had wanted to make fun of me and make me lose my footing. He was clever all right, and he could talk, but he couldn't put that one over, not on me!

in that case 이런 경우에 하나님이 이 이야기에 적합한가? He=God

suspect=doubt
사역동사(make)+목+동/원: make me lose my footing 나를 골탕 먹이다
he could talk ~ on me 그는 그런 이야기는 할 수 있었지만, 나에게 그의 사상을 받아들이도록 강요할 수는 없었다.

I had never before given as much thought to a biblical 성경의 story or to any other story. And for a long time I had not forgotten Franz Kromer as completely; for hours, for a whole evening in fact. At home I read the story once more as written in the Bible. It was brief and unambiguous 명확한; it was quite mad to look for a special, hidden meaning. At that rate every murderer could declare 공언하다 that he was God's darling! No, what Demian had said was nonsense. What pleased me was the ease and grace **with which** he was able to say such things, as though everything were self-evident 자명한; and then the look in his eyes!

ambiguous 모호한

at that rate 그런 식으로는

the ease and grace 편안함과 우아함

Something was very wrong with me, though; my life was in very great disorder. I had lived in a wholesome and clean world, had been a kind of Abel myself, and now I was stuck deeply in the "other world," had fallen and sunk very low — yet it hadn't basically been my fault! How was I to consider that? And now a memory flashed 떠오르다 within me **that** for a moment almost left me breathless. On that fatal 숙명적인 evening when my misery had begun, there had been that matter with my father. There, for a moment, I had seen through him and his world of light and wisdom and had felt nothing but contempt 경멸 for it. Yes, at that moment I, who was Cain and bore the mark, had imagined that this sign was

wholesome=sound 건강한, 건전한

be stuck ~에 빠져 있다

was to = could 내가 그러한 일을 어떻게 생각해 낼 수 있었겠는가?
주격 관/대 that:
a memory that left me ~ 아버지가 나의 심각한 문제를 직시하지 못하고 진흙이 묻은 신발에 대해서 꾸중하던 사건

nothing but=only

not a mark of shame and that because of my evil and misfortune I stood higher than my father and the pious, the righteous.

I had not experienced the moment in this form, in clearly expressed thoughts, but all of this had been contained within it; **it had been** the eruption 분출 of emotions, of strange stirrings 동요, **that** hurt me yet filled me with pride at the same time.

When I considered how strangely Demian had talked about the fearless and the cowardly, what an unusual meaning he had given the mark Cain bore on his forehead, how his eyes, his remarkable adult eyes had lit up, **the question** flashed through my mind **whether** Demian himself was not a kind of Cain. Why does he defend Cain unless he feels an affinity 동족관계 with him? Why does he have such a powerful gaze 시선? Why does he speak so contemptuously 경멸하듯 of the "others," of the timid who actually are the pious, the chosen ones of the Lord?

I could not bring these thoughts to any conclusion 결론. A stone had been dropped into the well 우물, the well was my youthful soul. And for a very long time this matter of Cain, the fratricide 형제 살해, and the "mark" formed the point of departure 출발점 for all my attempts 시도 at comprehension 이해, my doubts and my criticism 비판.

I noticed that Demian exerted equal fascination over the other students. I hadn't told anyone about his version of the story of Cain, but the others seemed to be interested in him, too. At any rate, many rumors were in circulation about the "new boy." If I could only remember them all now, each one would throw some light on him and could be interpreted 설명되다. I remember first that Demian's mother was reported to be wealthy

the pious, the righteous
신앙심이 깊고 정의로운 사람

in this form 이런 형태로

within it
이런 사고의 형태 속에
it is A that 강조 구문:
-한 것은 바로 A이다

the fearless
두려움이 없는 자
the cowardly 비겁한 자
the mark (which) Cain
bore 카인이 지닌 표식

the question whether
~인지 아닌지에 대한 의문

the timid 겁쟁이들
the chosen ones of ~
신에 의해 선택받은 자들

exert equal fascination
~에게 동등한 매력을 발휘하다

be in circulation about
~에 관한 소문이 돌다
If I could ~ on him
지금 그 소문들을 기억해 낼
수 있다면, 각각의 소문들은
그가 어떤 사람인지에 대해
밝혀 줄 텐데.

and also, supposedly 아마, neither she nor her son ever attended church. One story **had it that** they were Jewish but they might equally well have been secret Mohammedans 이슬람교인. Then there was Max Demian's legendary physical prowess 용맹. But this could be corroborated 확인되다: when the strongest boy in Demian's class had taunted 비웃다 him, **calling** him a coward when he refused to fight back, Demian had humiliated him. Those who were present told that Demian had grasped the boy with one hand by the neck and squeezed until the boy went pale; afterwards, the boy had slunk away and had not been able to use his arm for a whole week. One evening some boys even claimed that he was dead. For a time everything, even the most extravagant assertions 터무니없는 주장 were believed. Then everyone seemed to have had their fill of Demian for a while, though not much later gossip again flourished 무성하다: some boys reported that Demian was intimate 친밀한 with girls and that he "knew everything."

Meanwhile 한편, my business with Kromer took its inevitable 피할 수 없는 course. I couldn't escape him, for even when he left me alone for days I was still bound to him. He haunted my dreams and what he failed to perpetrate on me in real life, my imagination let him do to me in those dreams **in which** I was completely his slave. I have always been a great dreamer; in dreams I am more active than in my real life, and these shadows sapped me of health and energy. A recurring nightmare 반복되는 악몽 was **that** Kromer always maltreated 학대하다 me, spit and knelt on me and, what was worse, led me on to commit 범하다 the most horrible crimes — or, rather, not so much led me on as compelled me through sheer force of persuasion. The worst of these dreams, **from**

---

neither A nor B
A도 B도 ~가 아니다
A has it that B:
A에 따르면 B라고 한다
equally well 마찬가지로

분사구 calling:
그를 ~라 부르면서
humiliate 창피를 주다

grasp=hold, catch

squeeze=press tightly

slink away 빠져나가다
slink-slunk-slunk

have one's fill of
~에 대해 충분히 알다

not much later 머지않아

be bound to ~에 묶여 있다

haunt my dreams
나의 꿈에 나오다
perpetrate on
~에게 나쁜 짓을 하다

sap A of B:
B에게서 A를 짜내다

lead A on to B
A가 B하도록 이끌다

not so much A as B:
A하기보다는 B하다
순전한 설득의 힘으로 내가
~하도록 강요했다

which I awoke half-mad, had to do with a murderous assault 잔인한 공격 on my father. Kromer whetted a knife, put it in my hand; we stood behind some trees in an avenue 가로수길 and lay in wait for someone, I did not know whom. Yet when this someone approached and Kromer pinched my arm to let me know that this was the person I was to stab 찌르다— it was my father. Then I would awake.

Although I still drew a connection between these events and the story of Cain and Abel, I gave little thought to Max Demian. When he first approached me again, it was, oddly enough 이상하게도, also in a dream. For I was still dreaming of being tortured. Yet this time it was Demian who knelt on me. And — this was totally new and left a deep impression on me — everything I had resisted and that had been agony to me when Kromer was my tormentor I suffered gladly at Demian's hands, with a feeling compounded as much of ecstasy as of fear. I had this dream twice. Then Kromer regained his old place.

For years I have been unable to distinguish between what I experienced in these dreams and in real life. In any event 어쨌든, the bad relationship with Kromer continued and by no means came to an end after I had finally paid my debt out of any number of petty thefts. No, for now he knew of these new thefts since he asked each time where I had gotten the money, and I was more in bondage to him than ever. Often he threatened to tell everything to my father but even then my fear was hardly as great as my profound regret at not having done so myself at the very beginning. In the meantime 그동안, miserable though I was, I did not regret everything that happened, at least not all the time, and occasionally I even felt that everything had had to happen as it did.

---

have to do with
~와 관계가 있다
whet (칼을) 갈다

was to=should

draw a connection
between A and B: A와 B
간에 관련성을 이끌어 내다

it is ~ who (that) 강조구문
kneel-knelt-knelt on
~에게 무릎을 꿇다
무릎으로 나를 짓누르다
(목적어)+주+동 도치구조
=I suffered gladly
(everything I had ~ my
tormentor) at Demian's
hands
as much A as B:
두려움만큼이나 희열도 큰
뒤섞인 감정으로

distinguish between A and
B: A와 B 사이를 구분하다

by no means=never

petty thefts 사소한 도둑질

since he ~ than ever
그가 나의 돈의 출처를 계속
물었기 때문에 이 새로운
도둑질로 인해 그의 속박에서
벗어나지 못하다
be in bondage to
~에 속박되다

my fear ~ profound regret
두려움이 깊은 후회만큼
크지는 않았다.

though I was miserable
비참하긴 했지만
everything has ~ did
만사는 이렇게 될 수밖에
없다. 운명의 장난이다.

I was in the hands of fate and it was useless to try to escape.

Presumably 아마, my parents also were distressed 괴로운 by the state I was in. A strange spirit had taken hold of me, I no longer fitted into 적합하다 our community, once so intimate; yet often a wild longing 강렬한 갈망 came over me to return to it as to a lost paradise 실락원. My mother in particular treated me more like an invalid 환자 than a scoundrel 악당, but my true status 상태 within the family I was better able to judge from my sisters' attitude. Theirs was one of extreme indulgence 은혜, which made **it** plain 분명한 **that** I was considered a kind of madman, more to be pitied for his condition than blamed, but possessed by the devil nonetheless. They prayed for me with unusual fervor 열정 and I was infinitely miserable 한없이 비참한 when I realized the futility 무익 of these prayers. Often I felt a burning need for relief 구원, for genuine confession 진정한 고백, and yet sensed in advance that I would be unable to tell my mother or father, and explain everything properly 적절히. I knew **that** everything I said would be accepted sympathetically 동정적으로, **that** they would, yes, even feel sorry for me, but **that** they would not understand, **that** the whole thing would be regarded as a momentary aberration 순간적인 일탈, whereas 반면 in truth it was my fate.

I realize that some people will not believe that a child of little more than ten years is capable of having such feelings. My story is not intended for them. I am telling it to those who have a better knowledge of man. The adult who has learned to translate a part of his feelings into thoughts notices the absence of these thoughts in a child, and therefore comes to believe that the child lacks these experiences, too. Yet rarely in my life have I felt and suffered as deeply as at that time.

(관/대+be동사) 생략구조
=(which was) once so intimate

theirs=their attitudes

가목적어 it, 진목적어 that:
made it plain that ~
나는 집안에서 귀신이 들린 존재이기 때문에 책망받기 보다는 불쌍히 여겨저야 할 존재로 인식되다

sense=feel

접속사 that (목적어) 4개:
knew의 목적어

be capable of ~ing
=be able to 동사=can

be intended for
~를 위해서 의도되다

translate A into B:
A를 B로 해석하다
the adult 주어
notices 동사

부사+동사+주어 도치구조
=I have rarely felt and suffered in my life ~

One day it rained. Kromer had ordered me to meet him at the Burgplatz, and there I stood and waited, **shuffling** among the wet chestnut leaves that were still falling from the black wet trees. I had no money with me but I had managed to put aside two pieces of cake and had brought them along so as to be able to give Kromer something at least. By now I was used to standing in some corner and waiting for him, often for a very long time, and I accepted it the same way one learns to put up with the inevitable. Kromer showed up finally. He didn't stay long. He poked me in the ribs a few times, laughed, took the cake, even offered me a damp 축축한 cigarette (which, however, I did not accept), and was friendlier than usual.

"Yes," he said nonchalantly 태연하게 before going away, "before I forget it, you might bring your sister along the next time, the older one, what's her name."

I failed to get his point and made no reply. I only looked at him, surprised. "Don't you understand? You're to bring your sister."

"No, Kromer, that's impossible. I wouldn't be allowed to and she wouldn't come in any case." I was prepared for this new ruse 책략 or pretext 구실 of his. He did this often: demanded 요구하다 something impossible, frightened and humiliated 굴욕감을 주다 me, then gradually offered some bargain 흥정 as a way out, and I had to buy myself off with some money or a gift.

This time, however, it was altogether different. My refusal 거절 did not seem to make him angry at all.

"Well, anyway," he said in a matter-of-fact tone, "think it over. I'd like to meet your sister. We'll find a way one of these days. You could simply take her along on a walk and then I could join you. I'll give you a whistle

- 42 -

Burgplatz 부르크 광장

분사구 shuffling:
발로 ~를 휘저으며

so as to = in order to

be used to ~ing
=be accustomed to ~ing
~에 익숙하다

put up with=endure=
stand=bear 참다, 견디다
the inevitable
견딜 수 없는 것들

are to = should

as a way out
(부당한 요구에서) 빠져
나오는 방식으로
buy myself off 뇌물을 주다

사무적인 어조로 말하다
think over 곰곰이 생각하다

tomorrow, then we can talk about it some more."

After he had left, something of the nature 본질 of his request suddenly dawned on me. I was still quite ignorant 무지한 in these matters but I knew from hearsay that boys and girls when they grew older were able to do certain mysterious, repulsive 역겨운, forbidden 금지된 things together. And now I was supposed to — it suddenly flashed on me how monstrous 엄청난 his request was! I knew at once that I would never do it. But what would happen then? What revenge 복수 would Kromer take on me? I didn't dare think of it. This was the beginning of a new torture for me.

Inconsolable, I walked across the desolate square 황량한 광장, hands in my pockets. Further and greater agonies 고뇌 awaited me!

Suddenly a vigorous cheerful voice called me. I was startled and began to flee. Someone ran after me, a hand grasped me gently from behind. It was Max Demian.

"Oh, it's you," I said mistrustfully 믿지 못하겠다는 투로. "You gave me a terrible shock."

He looked down at me and never had his look been more adult, superior, the look of someone who could see through me. We had not spoken to each other for a long time.

"I feel sorry for you," he said in his polite yet decisive 단호한 manner. "Listen, you can't let yourself be frightened like that."

"Well, one can't always help it."

"So it seems. But look: if you practically go to pieces in front of someone who hasn't done you any harm, then that someone begins to think. He's surprised, he becomes inquisitive 호기심이 많은, he thinks you're

dawn on 생각이 떠오르다

know from hearsay
풍문/소문으로 알고 있다

I was supposed to (do certain ~ things)
이제 내가 그런 짓을 하기로 되어 있었다.

flash 불현 듯 떠오르다

(being) 생략 분사:
(Being) inconsolable
슬픔에 잠겨

await=wait for

=his look had never been

see through me
나를 꿰뚫어 보다

let ~ (be) frightened

cannot always help it
놀랄 수도 있지 뭘 그래.
goo to pieces
두려워 벌벌 떨다

then that someone ~
그러면 그 사람은 생각하겠지.

remarkably high-strung 신경질적인 and reaches the conclusion **that** people are always like that when they're deathly afraid. Cowards 겁쟁이 are constantly afraid, but you're not a coward, are you? Certainly, you're no hero either. There are some things you're afraid of, and some people, too. And **that** should never be, you should never be afraid of men. You aren't afraid of me? Or are you?"

"Oh, no, not at all."

"Exactly. But there are people you are frightened of?"

"I don't know. . . Why don't you let me be?" He kept pace with me — I had quickened my steps with thoughts of escaping — and I felt him glancing at me from the side.

"Let's assume 가정하다," he began again, "**that** I don't mean to do you any harm. At any rate, you've no need to be afraid of me. I'd like to try out an experiment on you. It might be fun and you might even learn something from it. Now pay attention! — You see, I sometimes practice an art known as thought reading. There's no black magic 흑마술 about it but if you don't know how it's done it can seem very uncanny 초자연적인. You can shock people with it, too. Now let's give it a try. Well, I like you, or I'm interested in you and would like to discover what goes on inside you. I've already taken the initial step in that direction: I've frightened you — so that you're nervous. There must be things and people that you're afraid of. If you are afraid of someone, the most likely reason is **that** this someone has something on you. For example, you've done something wrong and the other person knows it — he has a hold on you. You get it? Very clear, isn't it?"

I looked up helplessly at his face, **which** was as serious and intelligent as ever, and kind. Yet its detached severity 초연한 엄격함 lacked tenderness; impartiality 공정성 or something similar was visible in it. I was hardly aware of what was happening to me: he stood before me like a magician.

"Have you got it?" he asked once more. I nodded, **unable** to speak.

(being) 생략 분사:
(Being) unable to speak
말을 할 수 없어서

"I told you, reading other people's thoughts seems strange but it's perfectly natural. For instance, I could tell you almost exactly what you thought about me **the time** I told you the story of Cain and Abel. Well, this isn't the time to talk of that. I also think **it** possible **that** you dreamed about me once. But let's put that aside, too. You're bright and most people are stupid. I like talking to a bright fellow now and then, someone I can trust. You don't mind, do you?"

the time=when 접속사

가/목 it, 진/목 that
put that aside
그 이야기는 다음에 하자.

You don't mind, do you?
싫은 건 아니지?

"Of course not. But I don't understand. . ."

"Let's keep to our amusing experiment for the moment. So, we've discovered that boy S is easily frightened — he's afraid of someone — he probably shares a secret with this other person, a secret that makes him feel uneasy. Roughly speaking 대략 말해서, does this correspond to the facts?"

let's keep to
계속 ~을 해보자.

correspond to
내 말지 사실과 일치하지?

As though in a dream, I succumbed to his voice and influence. His voice seemed to come from within myself. And it knew everything. Did it know everything more clearly and better than I did myself?

succumb to 굴복하다

Demian slapped me firmly on the shoulder.

"So that's what it is. I thought it might be. Now just one more question: do you happen to know the name of the boy who left you back there at the Burgplatz?"

that's what it is.
내 짐작이 맞구나.

Burgplatz 부르크 광장

I was terrified. He had touched my secret.

"What boy? There wasn't any boy there, only me."

"Go on." He laughed. "What's his name?"

"Do you mean Franz Kromer?" I whispered.

He gave me a satisfied nod.

"Excellent. You're all right, we'll become friends yet.

But first I have to tell you something: this Kromer, or whatever his name is, his face tells me he's a first-rate bastard 가장 나쁜 악당. What do you think?"

"Yes," I sighed, "he's pretty bad. But he mustn't hear about this. For God's sake. He mustn't find out anything. Do you know him? Does he know you?"

"Relax. He's gone and he doesn't know me — not yet. But I'd like to meet him. He goes to public school, doesn't he?"

"Yes."

"What grade's he in?"

"The fifth. But don't say anything to him. Please."

"Don't worry, nothing will happen to you. I take it you don't want to tell me more about this Kromer?"

"I can't."

He was silent for a while.

"Too bad," he said. "We could have carried the experiment a stage further. But I don't want to get you all upset. However, you realize, don't you, **that** your fear of him is all wrong? Such fear can destroy us completely. You've got to get rid of it, you've simply got to, if you want to turn into someone decent 품위 있는. You understand that, don't you?"

"Certainly, you're completely right. . . But it's so complicated 복잡한. . . You've no idea. . ."

"You've seen that I know quite a few things about you, far more than you would have imagined. — Do you owe him any money?"

"Yes, that too. But that's not the main thing. I can't tell you, I just can't."

"Wouldn't it help if I gave you as much as you owe him?"

"No, that's not it. And you promise not to tell anyone about it? Not a word?"

"You can trust me, Sinclair. You can tell me your secret some other time."

"Never!" I shouted.

"As you like. All I meant was: perhaps you'll tell me more some other time. Voluntarily, of course. You don't think I would treat you the way Kromer does, do you?"

"Oh, no — but what do you know about that anyhow?"

"Nothing whatever. I've merely thought it over and I'd never do it Kromer's way, you can believe that. Besides, you don't owe me anything."

We did not speak for a long time, and I began to calm down, yet I found Demian's knowledge all the more puzzling.

"I'm going home now," he said and gathered his coat closer around him in the rain.

"There's just one more thing I'd like to say to you since we've gotten so far — you ought to get rid of this bastard! If there's no other way of doing it, kill him. It would impress and please me if you did! I'd even lend you a hand."

The story of Cain suddenly recurred to me, and I became afraid again. Everything began to seem **so** ominous 불길한 to me **that** I began to whimper 훌쩍이다. I was surrounded by too much that I didn't understand.

"All right." Max Demian smiled. "Go on home. We'll find a way, even though killing him would be the simplest. In cases like this, the simplest course is always the best. Your friend Kromer isn't the best friend to have."

I found my way home and **it** seemed to me **that** I had

owe somebody something
누군가에게 무언가를 빚지다

as you like sj 좋을 대로 해

what do you know ~
도대체 넌 그 일에 대해
얼마나 알고 있는 거야?
(I know) nothing whatever.
난 전혀 모른다.
think ~ over
~에 대해 곰곰이 생각하다

We did ~ calm down
오랜 침묵이 흘렀고 난
안정되기 시작했다.
find A B(puzzling):
A가 B하다고 생각하다
all the more 오히려, 더욱더

since we've gotten so far
우리가 이 만큼 왔기 때문에

recur to me
다시 나의 마음에 떠오르다

so ~ that 구조

been away for a year. Everything looked different. Something like a future, like hope, now separated me from Kromer. I was no longer alone. Only now did I realize how horribly alone I had been with my secret for weeks on end 계속. And at once I remembered a thought I had had several times before: **that** a confession to my parents would lighten my load but would not entirely relieve me of it. Now I had almost confessed, to another, to a stranger, and the sense of relief was like a fresh breeze.

Nonetheless, my fear was far from conquered and I was prepared for a long series of terrible wrangles 언쟁 with my enemy. That was why it seemed remarkable that matters took such a calm, such a discreet course.

For one day, for two, for a whole week there was no sound of Kromer's whistle near our house. I hardly dared believe it and I constantly lay in wait for the moment **when** suddenly, when least expected, he would reappear. He seemed to have vanished 사라지다. Mistrusting my new freedom, I refused to believe in it, that is, until I finally ran into Franz Kromer. When he saw me he flinched 움찔하다, his face twitched, and he turned away so as to avoid meeting me.

It was an unprecedented moment for me! My enemy fleeing from me, my devil afraid of me! A thrill of happy surprise overwhelmed me.

One day I ran into Demian again. He was waiting for me in front of school.

"Hello," I said.

"Good morning, Sinclair. I only wanted to hear how things were going. Kromer isn't bothering you any more, is he?"

"Is that your doing? How did you manage it? I don't

remember a thought **that** a confession to my ~

relieve A of B:
A에게서 B를 덜어주다

far from (being) conquered
정복되려면 아직 멀었다
be prepared for
~할 준비가 되어 있다
matters take ~ course
사태가 조용하고 신중하게 흘러가다

접속사 when (it was) least expected 전혀 예상치 못할 때
관계부사 when:
the moment when he would reappear
완료부정사 to have -pp
=It seemed that he had vanished.

unprecedented
선례가 없었던

- 48 -

understand it at all. He's staying away altogether."

"That's good. If he should turn up again — I don't think he will, but he's quite ruthless 무자비한— just tell him not to forget Max Demian."

"But what's the connection? Did you pick a fight and beat him up?"

connection 상관관계, 연관

"No, that's not my way of doing things. I merely talked to him **as** I did to you and was able to make **it** clear to him **that** it is to his advantage 이익 to leave you alone."

접속사 as: ~하듯이, 처럼

가/목 it, 진/목 that

"You didn't pay him any money, I hope."

"No, that's your method."

He evaded all my questions, **leaving** me with the same uneasy feeling toward him I'd had before: a strange mixture of gratitude 감사 and awe 경외, admiration 감탄 and fear, sympathy 연민 and inward resistance 저항.

분사구 leaving: ~남긴 채
목적격 관/대 (that) 생략:
feeling (that) I'd had ~

I decided to seek him out and talk at length about all these matters, as well as about the Cain business. But it did not happen that way. Gratitude is not a virtue 미덕 I believe in, and to me **it** seems hypocritical 위선적인 **to** expect it from a child. Thus my total ingratitude 배은망덕 toward Max Demian does not astonish me too much. Today I have no doubt whatever 전혀 that I **would have been** sick and **ruined** for life **had he not freed** me from Kromer's clutches 손아귀. Even at that time I was conscious **that** this liberation 해방 was the greatest experience of my life — but the liberator 해방자 himself I deserted as soon as he had performed his miracle.

seek out = meet or visit
at length 길게, 상세히

B as well as A:
A 뿐만 아니라 B도
목적격 관/대 (that) 생략:
a virtue (that) I believe in
it 가주어, to 진주어

astonish=surprise=startle

if 생략 가정법 과거완료:
=if he had not freed me
~하지 않았더라면, ~했을
것이다

목적어 도치구조 =
I deserted the liberator
himself.

As I have said, ingratitude does not surprise me. What does startle me, in retrospect, is my lack of curiosity. How was I able to go on living a single day without trying to come nearer to the secret which Demian had revealed 드러내다 to me? How was **it** I did not want to hear more about Cain, more about Kromer, more about

접속사 as: ~했듯이

in retrospect 회고해 보니

가주어 it, 진주어 that:
How was it (that) I did not
want 어떻게 ~할 수 있었지?

- 49 -

Demian's ability to read other peopled thoughts?

It is almost incredible, and yet it was so. I suddenly found myself extricated from a demonic labyrinth 악마의 미로. I again saw the world bright and joyful before me and no longer succumbed to fits of suffocating fear. The spell 마법 was broken, I was no longer damned and tormented. I was a schoolboy again, and my whole being sought to regain its peaceful equilibrium 평정 as quickly as possible, **making** a particular effort to repel and forget the ugly, threatening things I had come to know. The whole episode of my guilt and fright 죄와 공포 slipped from my memory with incredible speed and without apparently leaving any scars 상처 or deep impressions 인상 behind.

However, today I can understand why I strained to forget my savior 구세주 so quickly. I fled from the valley of sorrow, my horrible bondage 속박 to Kromer, with all the strength at the command of my injured soul: back to **where** I had been happy and content 만족한, back to the lost paradise that was opening up again now, back to the light, untroubled world of mother and father, my sisters, the smell of cleanliness, and the piety 신앙심 of Abel.

Already, the day after my short talk with Demian, when I was fully convinced at last of having regained my freedom and no longer feared losing it again, I did what I had wanted to do so often and desperately before — I confessed. I went to my mother, I showed her the damaged piggy bank **filled with** play money and I told her for how long I had bound myself through my own guilt to an evil tormentor. She did not understand everything **but** she saw; she saw my changed expression, heard the change in my tone of voice, and felt that I was cured and had been restored to her.

And now began the feast of my readmittance 재입장 to

find+목적어+목적보어 5형식: extricated=rescued 구출된
(주격 관/대+be) 생략구조: the world (which was) bright and joyful ~
fits of suffocating fear 숨 막히는 공포의 발작
dammed=cursed 저주받은

equilibrium=balance
분사구 making: ~하면서

come to know 알게 되다

without ~ing ~하지 않고

strain to ~하려고 안간힘을 쓰다

at the command of ~의 명령에 따라
관계부사 where: ~한 곳 (the place) where

be convinced of ~를 확신하다

desperately 몹시, 지독하게

(주격 관/대+be) 생략구조: piggy bank (which was) filled with play money
bind-bound-bound
bind A to B: A를 B에 속박하다
유사관계대명사 but=that ~ not=everything that she didn't see

도치구조

the fold, the return of the Prodigal Son. Mother took me to my father, the story was repeated, there were questions and exclamations 절규 of surprise, both parents stroked my head and breathed sighs of relief after the long period of oppression 중압감. Everything was marvelous 놀라운, everything happened **as** the stories I had read said they would, everything resolved itself in wonderful harmony.

I drugged myself on the satisfaction of having regained my peace of mind and the confidence of my parents, I became a most exemplary boy at home, played more than ever with my sisters and during the devotional periods 기도시간 sang all my favorite hymns with the fervor 열정 of one who has been saved, who has been converted 개종하다. It came from my heart, there was nothing false about it.

Still, not everything was back in order. And this is the fact **that** really accounts for my neglect 무관심 of Demian. I **should have confessed** to him. The confession **would have been** less emotional and touching, but it **would have been** far more fruitful. I had returned to my former, my Edenic world. This was not Demian's world, and he **would never have been** able to fit into it. He too — though differently from Kromer — was a tempter 유혹자; he, too, was a link to the second, the evil world **with which** I no longer wanted to have anything to do. I did not want to sacrifice Abel to glorify 찬양하다 Cain, not just now when I had once more become Abel.

Those were the superficial 피상적인 reasons. The inner ones, however, were as follows: I was free of Kromer and the devil's hands but through no power or effort of my own. I had tried to pass through the labyrinth 미궁 of the world but the way had proved too intricate 복잡한 for me.

fold-양의 우리
탕아의 귀환 축제

접속사 as: ~하듯이
접속사 (that) 생략구조
said (that) they would happen 모든 일들이 성경에서 말하는 대로 일어났고, 순조롭게 해결되었다.

I drugged my self on ~ ~했다는 만족감에 빠졌다

주격 관/대 that:
account for=explain
should have confessed:
고해했어야 했는데 (사실은 하지 못했다)
가정법 과거완료: 만약 고백 했더라면, ~했을 텐데...

Edenic ~ 에덴동산의 세계
가정법 과거완료:
(If he had been in Edenic world), he would never have been able to fit ~

with 전치사 + 관/대:
have anything to do with ~와 관계가 있다

not just now when ~ Abel 이제 막 다시 한 번 더 아벨이 된 지금은 ~ 아니다

ones = reasons

through no power ~ 나 자신의 힘과 노력에 의해서가 아니다

Now that a friendly hand had extricated 해방하다 me, I retreated 후퇴하다, looking neither to the left nor to the right, but went straight to my mother's lap and the security 안전 of a pious, sheltered childhood. I turned myself into someone younger, more dependent, more childish than I was. I had to replace my dependence 의존 on Kromer with a new one, for I was unable to walk alone. So, in the blindness 맹목 of my heart, I chose to be dependent on my father and mother, on the old, cherished "world of light," though I knew by now that it was not the only one. If I had not followed this course I would have had to bank on Demian and entrust myself to him. That I did not do so at the time seemed to me to be the result of my justifiable suspicion of his strange ideas; in reality it was entirely because of my fear. For Demian would have been far more exacting 엄한 than my parents; he would have tried to make me more independent by using persuasion, exhortation, mockery, and sarcasm. I realize today that nothing in the world is more distasteful 싫은 to a man than to take the path that leads to himself.

Yet six months later I could not resist the temptation and I asked my father during a walk what one was to make of the fact that some people considered Cain a better person than Abel.

He was much taken aback and explained that this was an interpretation entirely lacking in originality 독창성, that it had already arisen in Old Testament times and had been taught by a number of sects 종파, one of which were called the "Cainites." But of course this mad doctrine 학설 was merely an attempt on the part of the devil to destroy our faith, for, if one believed that Cain was right and Abel in the wrong, then it followed that God had

접속사 now that: because
분사구 looking:
좌우도 돌아보지 않고
the security ~ childhood
신성하고 보호를 받는 어린
시절의 안전함

replace A with B:
A를 B로 대체하다
접속사 for: 왜냐하면
be dependent on
~에 의존하다

cherished 소중하게 지켜져 온

가정법 과거완료: 만약 ~
했더라면, ~ 했을 텐데
bank on=depend on
entrust A to B:
A를 B에게 맡기다
접속사 that: ~ 한 것은
justifiable suspicion
타당한/정당한 의심

가정법 과거완료

persuasion 설득
exhortation 간곡한 권고
mockery 조롱, 비웃음
sarcasm 비꼼, 풍자

주격 관/대 that:
자기 자신에게로 이르는 길로
인도하려는 자가 가장 싫다

resist the temptation
유혹을 물리치다
I asked - the fact that ~
사람들이 ~라는 사실에 대해
어떻게 생각하는 지 물었다.

taken aback=surprised

arise-arose-arisen
발생하다, 일어나다
a number of=many

Cáinites 카인교도

접속사 for: 왜냐하면
then it followed that
~를 인정하는 것이다

made a mistake; in other words, the God of the Bible
was not the right and only one, but a false God. Indeed,
the Cainites had taught and preached something of the
sort. However, this heresy 이단 had long since disappeared
from the face of the earth and he was only surprised
that a school friend of mine **should have heard** anything
about it. He warned me most seriously against harboring
such ideas.

should have heard ~
(듣지 말았어야 할 것을)
들었다는 것에 놀랐다
harboring=having

Chapter III
Among Thieves

Source: https://en.wikipedia.org/wiki/Crucifixion_of_Jesus

III. Among Thieves

If I wanted to, I could recall many delicate moments from my childhood: the sense of being protected **that** my parents gave me, my affectionate nature, simply living a playful, satisfied existence in gentle surroundings. But my interest centers on the steps that I took to reach myself. All the moments of calm, the islands of peace whose magic I felt, I leave behind in the enchanted distance. Nor do I ask to ever set foot there again.

That is why — as long as I dwell on my childhood — I will emphasize the things **that** entered it from outside, **that** were new, **that** impelled me forward or tore me away. These impulses 충동 always came from the "other world" and were accompanied by fear, constraint 압박, and a bad conscience 양심의 가책. They were always revolutionary 혁명적 and threatened the calm in which I would gladly have continued to live.

Then came those years in which I was forced to recognize the existence of a drive 충동 within me that had to make itself small and hide from the world of light. The slowly awakening sense of my own sexuality 성적관심 overcame me, **as** 듯이 it does every person, **like** an enemy and terrorist, **as** 로써 something forbidden, tempting and sinful. **What** my curiosity 호기심 sought, **what** dreams, lust 욕정 and fear created — the great secret of puberty 사춘기 — did not fit at all into my sheltered 안전한 childhood. I behaved like everyone else. I led the double life of a child who is no longer a child. My conscious self lived within the familiar and sanctioned 인정받은 world, it denied the new world that dawned within me. Side by side with this I lived in a world of dreams, drives, and desires of a chthonic nature, **across which** my conscious self

delicate 우아한, 섬세한

목적격 관/대 that 2개

affectionate nature 다정한 본성

center on ~에 집중되다
(목적어) 도치구조: I leave behind (all the moment ~ felt)
in the enchanted distance 신비로운 아득히 먼 곳
Nor+조동사+주어+동사 (도치)
ask=want
dwell on ~를 떠올리다

it=my childhood
주격 관/대 that 3개:
the things that ~
impel A forward B: B를 향하도록 A를 몰아대다
tear A away from B A를 B로부터 분리시키다
(B: the world of good)
be accompanied by ~를 동반하다

도치구조:
came those years
a drive **that** had to ~
빛의 세계에서는 축소하거나 은폐하고자 했던 충동

overcame=conquered
does=overcomes

관/대 what: ~한 것

fit into ~에 적합하다

dawn 나타나기 시작하다
side by side with this 이러한 것과 동시에
chthonic nature 심연(지하세계)의 본성

- 55 -

desperately built its fragile bridges, for the childhood world within me was falling apart. Like most parents, mine were no help with the new problems of puberty, **to which** no reference was ever made. All they did was take endless trouble in supporting my hopeless attempts to deny reality and to continue dwelling in a childhood world that was becoming more and more unreal. I have no idea whether parents can be of help, and I do not blame mine. It was my own affair to come to terms with myself and to find my own way, and like most well-brought-up children, I managed it badly.

Everyone goes through this crisis. **For** the average person this is the point **when** the demands of his own life come into the sharpest conflict with his environment, **when** the way forward has to be sought with the bitterest means at his command. Many people experience the dying and rebirth — which is our fate — only this once during their entire life. Their childhood becomes hollow and gradually collapses 무너지다, everything they love abandons 떠나다 them and they suddenly feel surrounded by the loneliness and mortal cold of the universe. Very many are caught forever in this impasse, and for the rest of their lives cling painfully to an irrevocable past, the dream of the lost paradise — which is the worst and most ruthless of dreams.

But let me return to my story. The sensations and dream images announcing the end of my childhood are too many to be related in full 충분히. The important thing was that the "dark world," the "other world," had reappeared. **What** Franz Kromer had once been was now part of myself. Several years had gone by **since** the episode with Kromer. That dramatic time **filled with** guilt lay far in the past and seemed like a brief nightmare

my conscious self ~
나의 의식적 자아는 이러한
세계를 가로지르는 불안한
다리를 지었다.
mine=my parents

made a reference to
~에 대해 언급하다
take endless trouble in
~하려고 끝없이 애쓰다

come to terms with
~와 타협하다

go through=experience
전치사 for: ~에게
관계부사 when 2개:
~하는 시점/때이다
come into the sharpest
conflict with ~와 가장
첨예하게 충돌하다
with the bitterest means
가장 혹독한 방법으로
at one's command
~의 명령에 따라서

hollow=empty, false

목적격 관/대 (that) 생략:
everything (that) they love

mortal cold 치명적인 추위

impasse 막다른 골목, 난국

cling to ~에 달라붙다
irrevocable past
되돌릴 수 없는 과거

sensations
=feelings, emotions

too many to be related
너무 많아서 말할 수 없다

관/대 what :~한 것
이전에 프란츠였던 것
전치사 since: ~ 이후로

(주격 관/대+be) 생략구조:
time (which was) filled ~

that had quickly vanished 사라지다.

Franz Kromer had long since gone out of my life, I hardly noticed when I happened to meet him in the street. The other important figure in my little tragedy, Max Demian, was never to go out of my life again entirely. Yet for a long time he merely stood at its distant fringes 가장자리, visible but out of effective range. Only gradually did he come closer, again **radiating** strength and influence.

out of effective range
영향을 미치지 못하는
only 부사+조동사+주어+동사
radiating: ~을 발산하면서

I am trying to see what I can remember of Demian at that time. **It** is quite possible **that** I didn't talk to him once for a whole year or even longer. I avoided him and he did not impose himself on me in any way. The few instances that we met, he merely nodded to me. Sometimes it even seemed as though his friendliness was faintly tinged with derision 조롱 or with ironic reproach 비꼬는 책망— but I may have imagined this. The experience **that** we had shared and the strange influence he had exerted on me at that time were seemingly forgotten by both of us.

impose A on B:
A를 B에게 강요하다

be tinged with
~의 기미/색을 띠다
may have imagined
상상 했을지도 모른다
influence (that) he had ~
exert influence on A:
A에게 영향력을 행사하다
seemingly 겉으로는

I can conjure up what he looked like and **now that** I begin to recollect, I can see **that** he was not so far away from me after all and **that** I did notice him. I can see him on his way to school, alone or with a group of older students, and I see him strange, lonely, and silent, **wandering** among them like a separate planet 분리된 행성, **surrounded** by an aura all his own, a law unto himself. No one liked him, no one was on intimate terms with him, except his mother, and this relationship, too, seemed not **that of** a child but of an adult. When they could, the teachers left him to himself; he was a good student but took no particular trouble to please anyone. Now and again we heard of some word, some sarcastic

conjure up
상상으로 불러내다
not that: ~ 해 보니
see that ~를 알다

분사구 wandering
떠돌아다니며
분사구 surrounded by
자신만의 분위기에 둘러싸여
be on intimate terms with
~와 친밀한 관계를 맺다

that of=relationship of

to himself=alone

take trouble to
~하려고 애쓰다

now and again=sometimes

comment 신랄한 의견 or retort 반박 he was rumored to have made to a teacher, and **which** ─ as gems of provocation 도발 and cutting irony 예리한 풍자─ left little to be desired.

As I close my eyes to recollect I can see his image rise up: where was that? Yes, I have it now: in the little alley before our house. One day I saw him standing there, notebook in hand, sketching. He was drawing the old coat of arms with the bird above our entrance. As I stood at the window behind the curtain and watched him, I was deeply astonished by his perceptive, cool, light-skinned face that was turned toward the coat of arms, the face of a man, of a scientist or artist, superior and purposeful, strangely lucid 맑은 and calm, and with knowing eyes.

And I could see him on another occasion. It was a few weeks later, also in a street. All of us on our way home from school were standing about a fallen horse. It lay in front of a farmer's cart still **harnessed** to the shaft, **snorting** pitifully with dilated nostrils and **bleeding** from a hidden wound **so** the white dust on one side of the street was stained 얼룩지다. **As** I turned away **nauseous** I beheld Demian's face. He had not thrust himself forward but was standing farthest back, at ease and as elegantly dressed as usual. His eyes seemed fixed on the horse's head and again showed that deep, quiet, almost fanatical yet dispassionate absorption. I could not help looking at him for a time and **it** was then **that** I felt a very remote and peculiar sensation. I saw Demian's face and I not only noticed that it was not a boy's face but a man's; I also felt or saw that it was not entirely the face of a man either, but had something feminine 여성스런 about it, too. Yet the face struck me at that moment **as** neither masculine nor childlike, neither old nor young, but

목적격 관/대 (that) 생략
retort (that) he was ~
소문에 의하면 그가 선생님께
했다는 비판이나 반박
which left little to be desired as gems of ~
그러한 것들은 ~로서 더 바랄
나위 없이 훌륭했다
I have it now.
이제 나는 그곳에 있다.

old coat of arms
낡은 문장 (상징적 새나 동물)

preceptive 통찰력이 있는

분사구 3개:
달구지의 멍에를 매단 채
콧구멍으로 숨을 거칠게 내
쉬며, 피를 흘리며
접속사 so (that): 그래서

접속사 as=when
분사구 (being) nauseous:
매스꺼움을 느끼고
thrust oneself forward
~를 밀치고 앞으로 나오다

almost ~ absorption
거의 광적이지만 냉정한 몰입
ccould not help looking at
보지 않을 수 없었다
=could not but look at
It ~ that 강조용법

strike A as B:
A에게 B로서의 인상을 주다
neither A nor B

somehow a thousand years old, somehow timeless, **bearing** the scars of an entirely different history than we knew; animals could look like that, or trees, or planets — none of this did I know consciously, I did not feel precisely what I say about it now as an adult, only something of the kind. Perhaps he was handsome, perhaps I liked him, perhaps I also found him repulsive 불쾌한, I could not be sure of that either. All I saw was that he was different from us, he was like an animal or like a spirit or like a picture, he was different, unimaginably different from the rest of us.

My memory fails me and I cannot be sure whether what I have described has not to some extent been drawn from later impressions 인상.

Only several years later did I again come into closer contact with him. Demian had not been confirmed in church with his own age group **as** was the custom, and this again made him the object of wild rumors. Boys in school repeated the old story about his being Jewish, or more likely a heathen 이교도, and others were convinced that both he and his mother were atheists 무신론자 or belonged to some fabulous and disreputable sect 종파. In connection with this I also remember having heard him suspected of being his mother's lover. Most probably he had been brought up without any religious instruction whatever, but now this seemed to be in some way ominous 불길한 for his future. At rate, his mother decided to let him take Confirmation lessons after all, though two years later than his age group. So it came about that he went to the same Confirmation class as I did.

For a time I avoided him entirely. I wanted no part of him; he was surrounded by too many legends and secrets, but what bothered me most was a feeling of

bearing=having 분사구
scar 자국, 표식

부정어 도치구조:
none of this *did I know*

find+목+목/보: 5형식
목적격 관/대 (that) 생략:
=All (that) I was ~

memory fails me
더 이상 잘 기억이 나지 않다
to some extent 어느 정도

only 부사 도치구조:
only ~ *did I come* into

be confirmed
견진성사를 받다
as 도치구조: ~하듯
as *was the custom*

fabulous 믿을 수 없는
disreputable 평판이 나쁜
in connection with
~와 관련하여
remember ~ing
~했던 것을 기억하다
지각동사+목+목/보(pp):
heard him suspected 그가
의심을 받고 있다고 들었다.

at rate=at any rate

take confirmation lessons
견진성사 수업을 받다
=it happened that

being indebted to him **that** had not left me since the Kromer affair. I now had enough trouble with secrets of my own, **for** the Confirmation lessons coincided with my decisive enlightenment about sex, and **despite** all good intentions, my interest in religious matters was greatly diminished 감소하다. What the pastor 목사 discussed lay far away in a very holy but unreal world of its own; these things were no doubt quite beautiful and precious, but they were by no means as timely and exciting as the new things I was thinking about. **The more** indifferent this condition made me to the Confirmation lessons, **the more** I again became preoccupied with Max Demian. There seemed to be a bond between us, a bond that I shall have to trace as closely as possible. **As far as** I can remember, it began early one morning while the light still had to be turned on in our classroom. Our scripture teacher, a pastor, had embarked on the story of Cain and Abel. I was sleepy and listened with only half an ear. When the pastor began to hold forth loudly and urgently about Cain's mark I felt almost a physical touch, a warning, and looking up I saw Max Demian's face half turned round toward me from one of the front rows, with a gleaming eye that might express scorn as much as deep thought, you could not be sure. He looked at me for only a moment and suddenly I listened tensely 긴장하여 to the pastor's words, heard him speak about Cain and his mark, and deep within me I felt the knowledge **that** it was not as he was teaching it, **that** one could look at it differently, **that** his view was not above criticism.

This one minute re-established 재구축하다 the link between me and Demian. And how strange — hardly was I aware of a certain spiritual affinity 영적인 유사성, when I saw it

be indebted to
~에게 빚을 지다
a feeling **that** had not ~

접속사 for: 왜냐하면
coincide with
~와 동시에 일어나다
decisive enlightenment
결정적인 깨달음
전치사 despite=in spite of
~에도 불구하고

by no means=never

the 비교급, the 비교급
~하면 할수록 더욱 더 -하다
be indifferent to ~에
관심이 없다
be preoccupied with
~에 마음을 빼앗기다

접속사 as far as: ~하는 한

embark on=begin

hold forth loudly
큰 소리로 이야기하다
무언가가 나의 몸에 닿은
느낌이 들었다
지각동사+목+목/보(pp):
saw ~ turned

지각동사+목+목/보(pp):
heard ~ speak

동격의 접속사 that 3개:
~라는 깨달음을 얻었다
(카인의 이야기는) 목사님이
말씀하시는 대로가 아니다
be not above criticism
비판의 여지가 있다

부정어 hardly 도치
=I was hardly aware
hardly A, when B:
A하자마자, B하다

translated into physical closeness. I had no idea whether he was able to arrange it this way himself or whether it happened only by chance — I still believed firmly in chance at that time — but after a few days Demian suddenly switched seats in Confirmation class and came to sit in front of me (I can still recall it precisely: in the miserable poorhouse air 빈민들 냄새 of the overcrowded classroom I loved the scent of fresh soap **emanating** from his nape) and after a few days he had again changed seats and now sat next to me. There he stayed all winter and spring.

The morning hours had changed completely. They no longer put me to sleep or bored me. I actually looked forward to them. Sometimes both of us listened to the pastor with the utmost concentration 집중 and a glance 눈짓 from my neighbor could draw my attention to a remarkable story, an unusual saying. A further glance from him, a special one, could make me critical or doubtful.

Yet all too frequently we paid no attention. Demian was never rude to the teacher or to his fellow students. I never saw him indulge in the usual pranks, not once did I hear him guffaw or gossip during class, and he never incurred a teacher's reprimand. But very quietly, and more with signs and glances than whispering, he contrived to let me share in his activities, and these sometimes were strange.

For instance, he would tell me which of the students interested him and how he studied them. About some of them he had very precise knowledge. He would tell me before class: "When I signal with my thumb So-and-so will turn round and look at us, or will scratch his neck." During the period, when it had almost completely slipped

---

지각동사+목+목/보(pp): saw it translated into 영적인 유사성이 신체적 근접으로 바뀌는 것을 보았다.
by chance=accidentally 우연히

분사구 emanating from: 그의 목덜미에서 풍기는

look forward to 명/ing ~를 고대하다, 기다리다

a glance from ~ story 데미안의 눈길 한 번이면 나를 카인의 이야기에 주목 하게 만들었고,
A further glance ~ 그의 또 다른 특별한 눈길 한 번이면 내가 그 이야기에 대해 비판적이고 회의적이게 만들었다.
further=more

지각동사+목+목/보(동): saw ~ indulge in - indulge in pranks 못된 장난에 빠지다
부정어 not once 도치 not once *did I hear* 실속 없이 웃거나 험담하는 소리를 듣다
incur reprimand 비난을 초래하다
contrive to ~할 궁리를 하다
let ~ share

so-and-so 아무개, 어떤 녀석

when it had almost ~ 내가 완전히 그것에 대해 잊고 있었을 때

my mind, Max would suddenly make a significant gesture with his thumb. I would glance quickly at the student **indicated** and each time I saw him perform the desired movement 바라던 동작 like a puppet on a string. I begged Max to try this out on the pastor but he refused. Only once, when I came to class **unprepared** and told him that I hoped the pastor would not call on me that day, he helped me. The pastor looked for a student to recite an assigned catechism passage and his eyes **sweeping** through the room came to rest on my guilty face. Slowly he approached me, **his finger pointing** at me, **my name beginning** to form on his lips — when suddenly he became distracted or uneasy, pulled at his shut collar, stepped up to Demian, who was looking him directly in the eye and seemed to want to ask him something. But he turned away again, cleared his throat a few times, and then called on someone else.

Even though these tricks amused me, I began to notice gradually that my friend frequently played the same game with me. **It** would happen on my way to school **that** I would suddenly feel Demian walking not far behind me and when I turned around he was there in fact.

"Can you actually make someone think what you want him to?" I asked him.

He answered readily in his quiet, factual, and adult manner.

"No," he said, "I can't do that. You see, we don't have free will even though the pastor makes believe we do. A person can neither think what he wants to nor can I make him think what I want to. However, one can study someone very closely and then one can often know almost exactly what he thinks or feels and then one can also anticipate 예상하다 what he will do the next moment.

(주격 관/대+be) 생략구조:
student (who was) indicated
지적당한 학생
지각동사+목+목/보(동):
saw ~ perform

unprepared=without any preparation

an assigned catechism passage
할당된 교리문답 구절
(주격 관/대+be) 생략구조:
=his eyes (which were) sweeping ~ came to rest on 그의 시선이 ~에 멈추다
주어+분사구 2개:
손가락으로 나를 가리키면서 나의 이름을 부르려고 하면서
distracted 마음이 산만한

it 가주어, that 진주어

지각동사+목+목/보(동):
feel ~ walking

사역동사+목+동/원:
make ~ think

make believe 믿는 척하다
neither A nor B
nor 부정어 도치구조:
nor can I make him ~

It's simple enough, only people don't know it. Of course you need practice. For example, there is a species 종 of butterfly, a night-moth, **in which** the females are much less common than the males. The moths breed 번식하다 exactly like all animals, the male fertilizes 수정시키다 the female and the female lays the eggs. Now, if you take a female night-moth — many naturalists have tried this experiment — the male moths will visit this female at night, and they will come from hours away. From hours away! Just think! From a distance of several miles all these males sense the only female in the region. One looks for an explanation 설명 for this phenomenon 현상 but it is not easy. You must assume that they have a sense of smell of some sort like a hunting dog **that** can pick up and follow a seemingly inperceptible scent. Do you see? Nature abounds with such inexplicable things. But my argument is: if the female moths were as abundant 풍부한 as the males, the latter would not have such a highly developed sense of smell. They've acquired it only because they had to train themselves to have it. If a person **were to** concentrate 집중하다 all his will power on a certain end, then he **would** achieve it. That's all. And that also answers your question. Examine a person closely enough and you know more about him than he does himself."

It was on the tip of my tongue to mention "thought reading" 독심술 and to remind him of the scene with Kromer that lay so far in the past. But this, too, was strange about our relationship: neither he nor I ever alluded to the fact **that** several years before he had intruded 개입하다 so seriously into my life. It was **as though** nothing had ever been between us or **as though** each of us banked on it that the other had forgotten. On one or

in which
=and in the species

inperceptible scent
지각할 수 없는 냄새
abound with=be full of
inexplicable 설명할 수 없는

the former 전자-암컷
the latter 후자-수컷

가정법 과거:
were to=could

명령문 and 구조:
~해라, 그러면 ~할 것이다

be on the tip of one's
tongue 혀끝에서 맴돌다
remind A of B:
A에게 B를 상기시켜주다

allude to ~에 대해 언급하다
동격의 접속사 that:
~라는 사실
It was as though ~
마치 ~한 것 같았다
bank on it that ~를 믿다
the other 상대방

two occasions it even happened that we caught sight of Kromer somewhere in the street. Yet we neither glanced at each other nor said a word about him.

"What is all this about the will?" I asked. "On the one hand 한편, you say our will isn't free. Then again you say we only need to concentrate our will firmly on some end in order to achieve it. It doesn't make sense. If I'm not master of my own will 내 의지의 주인, then I'm in no position to direct it as I please."

He patted me on the back as he always did when he was pleased with me.

"Good that you ask," he said, laughing. "You should always ask, always have doubts. But the matter is very simple. If, for example, a night-moth **were to** concentrate its will on flying to a star or on some equally unattainable object, it **wouldn't** succeed. Only - it wouldn't even try in the first place 애초에. A moth confines its search to **what** has sense and value for it, on **what** it needs, **what** is indispensable to its life. And that's how a moth achieves the incredible — it develops a magic sixth sense, which no other creature has. We have a wider scope, greater variety of choice, and wider interests than an animal. But we, too, are confined to a relatively narrow compass 범위 which we cannot break out of. If I **imagined** that I wanted under all circumstances to get to the North Pole, to achieve it I **would** have to desire it strongly enough so that my whole being was ruled by it. **Once** that is the case, **once** you have tried something **that** you have been ordered to do from within yourself, then you'll be able to accomplish it, then you can harness 사용하다 your will to it like an obedient nag. But if I **were to** decide to will that the pastor should stop wearing his glasses, it **would** be useless. That would be

catch sight of =saw

What is all ~ will?
의지는 어떻게 되는 거지?
on the other hand
다른 한편

If I'm not master ~ please
내 의지의 주인이 내가
아니라면 내가 원하는 대로
나의 의지를 이끌 수 없다.

가정법 과거:
were to=intended to

confine A to B:
A를 B에 한정시키다

to what 3개: ~한 것에
be indispensable to
~에 없어서는 안 되다
the incredible 믿기 힘들
정도로 엄청난 것

be confined to:
~에 한정되어 있다

under all circumstances
어떤 환경에서도
가정법 과거

접속사 once: 일단 ~하면
목적격 관/대 that:
내가 ~하도록 명령받은 것

obedient nag
순종적인 늙은 말
가정법 과거:
were to=intended to

making a game of it. But at that time in the fall when I was resolved to move away from my seat in the front row, it wasn't difficult at all. Suddenly there was someone **whose** name preceded mine in the alphabet and **who** had been away sick until then and since someone had to make room for him it was me of course because my will was ready to seize 잡다 the opportunity at once."

"Yes," I said. "I too felt odd 이상한 at that time. From the moment **that** we began to take an interest in each other you moved closer and closer to me. But how did that happen? You did not sit next to me right away, first you sat for a while in the bench in front of me. How did you manage to switch once more?"

"It was like this: I didn't know myself exactly where I wanted to sit but I wanted to shift from my seat in the front row. I only knew that I wanted to sit farther to the back. It was my will to come to sit next to you but I hadn't become conscious of it as yet. At the same time your will accorded with 일치하다 mine and helped me. Only when I found myself sitting in front of you did I realize that my wish was only half fulfilled and that my sole aim was to sit next to you."

"But at that time no one fell ill, no one who had been ill returned, no new student joined the class."

"You're right. But at the time I simply did **as** I liked and sat down next to you. The boy **with whom** I changed seats was somewhat surprised but he let me do **as** I pleased. The pastor, too, once noticed that some sort of change had occurred. Even now something bothers him secretly **every time** he has to deal with me, **for** he knows that my name is Demian and that something must be wrong if I, a D, sit way in back in the S's. But **that** never penetrates 꿰뚫다 his awareness because my will opposes it and because I continuously place obstacles 장애 in his path. He keeps noticing that there's something wrong, then he looks at me and tries to puzzle it out. But I have a simple solution to that. **Every time** his eyes meet mine I stare him down. Very few people can stand that for long. All of them become uneasy. If you want something from someone and you look him firmly in both eyes and he doesn't become ill at ease, give up. You don't have a chance, ever! But that is very rare. I actually know only one person **where** it doesn't help me."

"Who is that?" I asked quickly.

He looked at me with narrowed eyes, as he did when he became thoughtful. Then he looked away and made no reply. Even though I was terribly curious I could not repeat the question.

I believe he meant his mother. He was said to have a very close relationship with her, yet he never mentioned her name and never took me home with him. I hardly knew what his mother looked like. Sometimes I attempted to imitate Demian and fix my will with such concentration 집중 on something that I was certain to achieve it. There were wishes that seemed urgent 긴급한 enough to me. But nothing happened; it didn't work. I could not bring myself to talk to Demian about it. I **wouldn't have been** able to confess my wishes to him. And he didn't ask either.

Meantime cracks 틈 had begun to appear in my religious faith. Yet my thinking, which was certainly much influenced by Demian, was very different from that of some of my fellow students who boasted 자랑하다 complete unbelief. On occasion 가끔 they would say **it** was ridiculous 우스운, unworthy of a person **to** believe in God, **that** stories like the Trinity 삼위일체 and Virgin Birth were

Keep noticing
계속 인지하다
puzzle out=solve

stare down 빤히 쳐다보다
stand=endure 견디다

become ill at ease
마음이 불편하다

관계부사 where
=and for him
그 사람을 상대로는 그런
수작은 통하지 않아.

A is said to
A가 ~하다는 소문이 들리다

가정법 과거완료

meantime 그러는 사이에

that of=thinking of

가주어 it, 진주어 to

would say **that**
Virgin Birth
성모마리아의 처녀수태

absurd, shameful. **It** was a scandal 창피 **that** we were still being fed such nonsense in our time. I did not share these views. Even though I had my doubts about certain points, I knew from my childhood the reality of a devout life 신앙생활, **as** my parents led it, and I knew also that this was neither unworthy nor hypocritical 위선의. On the contrary, I still stood in the deepest awe 경외 of the religious. Demian, however, had accustomed me to regard and interpret religious stories and dogma 교리 more freely, more individually, even playfully, with more imagination; at any rate, I always subscribed with pleasure to the interpretations he suggested. Some of it — the Cain business, for instance — was, of course, too much for me to stomach. And once during Confirmation class he startled me with an opinion that was possibly even more daring. The teacher had been speaking about Golgotha. The biblical account of the suffering and death of the Savior had made a deep impression on me since my earliest childhood. Sometimes, as a little boy, on Good Friday, for instance, **deeply moved** by my father's reading of the Passion to us, I would live in this sorrowful yet beautiful, ghostly, pale, yet immensely alive world, in Gethsemane and on Golgotha, and when I heard Bach's St. Matthew Passion the dark mighty glow of suffering in this mysterious world filled me with a mystical sense of trembling. Even today I find in this music and in his Actus Tragicus the essence of all poetry.

At the end of that class Demian said to me thoughtfully: 'There's something I don't like about this story, Sinclair. Why don't you read it once more and give it the acid test? There's something about it that doesn't taste right. I mean the business 사건 with the two thieves 도둑. The three crosses standing next to each other on the hill are most impressive, to be sure. But now comes this sentimental little treatise 감상적인 소논문 about the good thief. At first he was a thorough scoundrel 철저한 악당, had committed all those awful things and God knows what else, and now he dissolves in tears and celebrates such a tearful feast of self-improvement and remorse! What's the sense of repenting if you're two steps from the grave? I ask you. Once again it's nothing but a priest's fairy tale, saccharine 달콤한 and dishonest, touched up with sentimentality 감성 and given a highly edifying background. If you had to pick a friend from between the two thieves or decide which of the two you had rather trust, you most certainly wouldn't select that sniveling convert. No, the other fellow, he's a man of character 기질. He doesn't give a hoot for 'conversion,' which to a man in his position can't be anything but a pretty speech. He follows his destiny to its appointed end and does not turn coward and forswear 배신하다 the devil, who has aided and abetted 선동하다 him until then. He has character, and people with character tend to receive the short end of the stick in biblical stories. Perhaps he's even a descendant 후예 of Cain. Don't you agree?"

I was dismayed 당황한. Until now I had felt completely at home in the story of the Crucifixion. Now I saw for the first time with how little individuality, with how little power of imagination I had listened to it and read it. Still, Demian's new concept seemed vaguely sinister 사악한 and threatened to topple beliefs on whose continued existence I felt I simply had to insist. No, one could not make light of everything, especially not of the most sacred matters 신성시 되는 문제들.

As usual he noticed my resistance 저항 even before I

dissolve in tears
하염없이 목 놓아 울다
remorse 양심의 가책
죽음이 머지않았는데
뉘우치는 게 무슨 의미가
있는가?

be touched up with
~의 기미/낌새가 있다
edifying background
교화적인 배경

sniveling convert
울먹이는 개종자
개종에 대해 전혀 개의치
않다
nothing(=not anything) but
오직 ~일 뿐이다
to its appointed end
그것의 정해진 목적까지

character 개성, 기질
receive the short end of
the stick 불이익을 당하다

완전히 편안함을 느끼다
Crucifixion 예수의 십자가
수난 이야기

얼마나 형편없는 개성과
상상력을 지니고 그것을 읽고
들었던가.

존속이 지속되어야 한다고
느꼈던 믿음을 전복시키다

make light of
~을 가볍게 여기다

- 68 -

had said anything.

"I know," he said in a resigned tone of voice, "it's the same old story: don't take these stories seriously! But I have to tell you something: this is one of the very places that reveals the poverty of this religion most distinctly. The point is that this God of both Old and New Testaments 구약과 신약 is certainly an extraordinary figure 비범한 인물 but not **what** he purports to represent. He is all that is good, noble, fatherly, beautiful, elevated 숭고한, sentimental ─ true! But the world consists of something else besides. And what is left over is ascribed to the devil, this entire slice of world, this entire half is suppressed 억압된 and hushed up. In exactly the same way they praise God as the father of all life but simply refuse to say a word about our sexual life on which it's all based, **describing** it whenever possible **as** sinful, the work of the devil. I have no objection to worshiping this God Jehovah, far from it. But I mean we ought to consider everything sacred, the entire world, not merely this artificially separated half! Thus alongside the divine service we should also have a service for the devil. I feel that would be right. Otherwise 그렇지 않으면 you must create for yourself a God that contains the devil too and in front of which you needn't close your eyes when the most natural things in the world take place."

It was most unusual for him to become almost vehement 열렬한. But at once he smiled and did not probe any further. His words, however, touched directly on the whole secret of my adolescence 청년기, a secret I carried with me every hour of the day and of which I had not said a word to anyone, ever. What Demian had said about God and the devil, about the official godly and the suppressed devilish one, corresponded exactly to my own

in a resigned tone
체념한 듯한 목소리로

this 예수의 십자가 수난에 관한 이야기
poverty 결핍, 부족함
distinctly 뚜렷하게

성경의 신은 전지전능한 유일신이지만, 그 점이 신이 인간에게 보여주고자 의미한 것은 아니다.

be ascribed to
~에 귀속되다
세상의 온전한 조각
=이 온전한 절반
hush up 쉬쉬하며 숨기다

모든 생명이 근거하는 성생활에 대해서는 언급조차 하지 않는다.
it=sexual life
분사구 describing A sa B: A(성생활)를 B로 설명하면서
have no objection to ~ing
~에 반대하지 않는다
God Jehovah 여호아 신

alongside ~와 동시에

do not probe any further
더 이상 캐묻지 않다

official godly ~ devilish one
공인된 신의 세계와 억압된 악마의 세계
correspond exactly to
~와 정확히 일치하다

thoughts, my own myth, my own conception of the world as being divided into two halves — the light and the dark. The realization that my problem was one that concerned all men, a problem of living and thinking, suddenly swept over me and I was overwhelmed by fear and respect **as** I suddenly saw and felt how deeply my own personal life and opinions were immersed in the eternal stream of great ideas 거대한 사유의 영원한 흐름. Though it offered some confirmation 확인 and gratification 만족, the realization was not really a joyful one. It was hard and had a harsh taste because it implied 함축하다 responsibility and no longer being allowed to be a child; it meant standing on one's own feet 홀로서기를 하다.

Revealing a deep secret for the first time in my life, I told my friend of my conception of the "two worlds." He saw immediately that my deepest feelings accorded with his own. But it was not his way to take advantage of something like that. He listened to me more attentively 주의 깊게 than he had ever before and peered into my eyes so that I was forced to avert mine. For I noticed in his gaze again that strange animal-like look, **expressing** timelessness and unimaginable age.

"We'll talk more about it some other time," he said forbearingly 참을성 있게. "I can see that your thoughts are deeper than you yourself are able to express. But **since** this is so, you know, don't you, **that** you've never lived **what** you are thinking and **that** isn't good. Only the ideas that we actually live are of any value. You knew all along that your sanctioned world 허락된 세상 was only half the world and you tried to suppress the second half the same way the priests and teachers do. You won't succeed. No one succeeds in this **once** he has begun to think."

one that concerned ~
모든 인간들과 관련된 문제

The realization swept over
깨달음이 ~을 휩쓸고 지나가다
be overwhelmed by
~에 압도당하다
접속사 **as**=when
be immersed in
~에 깊이 빠져있다

분사구 **revealing**: 드러내면서

accord with ~와 일치하다

take advantage of
~을 이용하다

peer into ~를 들여다 보다

avert mine
나의 시선을 피하다
분사구 **expressing**:
시간을 초월하고 상상이
불가한 나이를 나타내는 모습

접속사 **since** =because

접속사 **that** (목적어)
관/대 **what**: ~한 것
대명사 **that**: 그것은

of value=valuable

(in) the same way
같은 식으로

접속사 **once**: 일단 ~하면

This went straight to my heart.

"But there are forbidden 금지된 and ugly things in the world!" I almost shouted. "You can't deny that. And they are forbidden, and we must renounce 포기하다 them. Of course I know that murder and all kinds of vices exist in the world but should I become a criminal just because they exist?"

"We won't be able to find all the answers today," Max soothed 달래다 me. "Certainly you shouldn't go kill somebody or rape a girl, no! But you haven't reached the point **where** you can understand the actual meaning of 'permitted' and 'forbidden.' You've only sensed part of the truth. You will feel the other part, too, you can depend on it. For instance, for about a year you have had to struggle with a drive 충동 **that** is stronger than any other and **which** is considered 'forbidden.' The Greeks and many other peoples, on the other hand 다른 한 편, elevated 숭배하다 this drive, made it divine and celebrated it in great feasts. What is forbidden, in other words, is not something eternal 불멸의; it can change. Anyone can sleep with a woman as soon as he's been to a pastor with her and has married her, yet other races do it differently, even nowadays. That is why each of us has to find out for himself what is permitted and what is forbidden -forbidden for him. It's possible for one never to transgress 어기다 a single law and still be a bastard. And vice versa. Actually it's only a question of convenience. Those who are too lazy and comfortable to think for themselves and be their own judges obey the laws. Others sense their own laws within them; things are forbidden to them **that** every honorable man will do any day in the year and other things are allowed to them **that** are generally despised. Each person must stand on

관계부사 **where**=at which

주격 관/대 **that, which**; 선행사 a drive를 수식

in other words 다시 말해서

a question of convenience 편의상의 문제

obey 본동사

목적격 관/대 **that**: things that every honorable
주격 관/대 **that**: other things that are ~
be despised 멸시 당하다

his own feet."

Suddenly he seemed to regret having said so much and fell silent. I could already sense what he felt at such moments. Though he delivered his ideas in a pleasant and perfunctory 형식적인 manner, he still could not stand 견디다 conversation for its own sake, **as** he once told me. In my case, however, he sensed — besides genuine 진짜의 interest — too much playfulness, too much sheer 순수한 pleasure in clever gabbing 수다, or something of the sort; in short, a lack of complete commitment 완벽한 진지함.

As I reread the last two words I have just written — complete commitment — a scene leaps to mind, the most impressive I ever experienced with Max Demian in those days when I was still half a child.

Confirmation day 견진성사일 was approaching and our lessons had the Last Supper 최후의 만찬 for their topic. This was a matter of importance to the pastor and he took great pains explaining it to us. One could almost taste the solemn 엄숙한 mood during those last hours of instruction 가르침. And of all times **it** had to be now **that** my thoughts were farthest from class, **for** they were fixed on my friend. While I looked ahead to being confirmed, which was explained to us as a solemn acceptance 수용 into the community of the church, I could not help thinking that the value of this religious instruction consisted for me not in what I had learned, but in the proximity 근접 and influence of Max Demian. **It** was not into the church **that** I was ready to be received but into something entirely different — into an order of thought and personality 개성 **that** must exist somewhere on earth and **whose** representative 대표자 or messenger I took to be my friend.

I tried to suppress this idea — I was anxious to involve

he could not stand ~
단순히 말만 주고받는 대화는 견디지 못하다
접속사 as: ~듯이
besides=in addition to

접속사 as=when
a scene leaps to mind
어떤 장면이 마음에 떠오르다

a matter of importance
=very important

it is ~ that 강조 구문:
내 생각이 수업과 가장 동떨어진 때는 바로 그때였음에 틀림없다.
접속사 for: 왜냐하면
they=my thoughts
look ahead to ~를 앞두다
견진성사는 교회라는 공동체 안으로 엄숙하게 받아들인다는 의식이다.

consist not in A but in B:
A가 아니라 B에 존재하다

it is ~ that 강조 구문:
not into A, but into B, into C
A속으로가 아니라 B, C속으로

주격 관/대 that:
an order ~ that must
소유격 관/대 whose:
an order whose representative
order 사상과 개성의 교단
take A to B: 그 교단의 대표자가 데미안으로 생각되다

myself in the Confirmation ceremony with a certain dignity 위엄, and this dignity seemed not to agree very well with my new idea. Yet, no matter what I did, the thought was present and gradually it became firmly linked with the approaching ceremony. I was ready to enact 규정하다 it differently from the others, for it was to signify 의미하다 my acceptance into a world of thought **as** I had come to know it through Demian. On one of those days it happened that we were having an argument just before class. My friend was tight-lipped 말수가 적은 and seemed to take no pleasure in my talk, which probably was self-important 거만한 as well as precocious 조숙한.

접속사 **as**: ~한 대로

"We talk too much," he said with unwonted seriousness. "Clever talk is absolutely worthless. All you do in the process is lose yourself. And to lose yourself is a sin. One has to be able to crawl completely inside oneself, like a tortoise 거북."

unwonted 이례적인, 드문

완전히 자신에게로 파고들다

Then we entered the classroom. The lesson began and I made an effort to pay attention. Demian did not distract 혼란시키다 me. After a while I began to sense something odd from the side where he sat, an emptiness or coolness or something similar, as though the seat next to me had suddenly become vacant. When the feeling became oppressive 답답한 I turned to look.

There I saw my friend sitting upright, his shoulders **braced** back as usual. Nonetheless, he looked completely different and something emanated 발산하다 from him, something surrounded him **that** was unknown to me. I first thought he had his eyes closed but then saw they were open. Yet they were not focused on anything, it was an unseeing gaze — they seemed transfixed with looking inward or into a great distance. He sat there completely motionless, not even seeming to breathe 숨쉬다;

분사구 (being) 주어 **braced**:
그의 어깨를 활짝 펴고

something that was ~

사역동사+목+목/보(pp):
have his eyes closed

transfixed with looking ~
보느라 고정된

his mouth might have been carved from wood or stone. His face was pale, uniformly pale like a stone, and his brown hair was the part of him **that** seemed closest to being alive. His hands lay before him on the bench, lifeless and still as objects, like stones or fruit, pale, motionless yet not limp, but like good, strong pods sheathing a hidden, vigorous life.

I trembled at the sight. Dead, I thought, almost saying it aloud. My spellbound 넋을 잃은 eyes were fixed on his face, on this pale stone mask, and I felt: this is the real Demian. When he walked beside me or talked to me — **that** was only half of him, someone **who** periodically plays a role, adapts himself 순응하다, **who** out of sheer complaisance does **as** the others do. The real Demian, however, looked like this, as primeval, animal, marble, beautiful and cold, dead yet secretly filled with fabulous life. And around him this quiet emptiness 적막한 공허, this ether, interstellar space 우주 공간, this lonely death!

Now he has gone completely into himself, I felt, and I trembled. Never had I been so alone. I had no part in him; he was inaccessible 접근불가의; he was more remote from me than if he **had been** on the most distant island in the world.

I could hardly grasp 이해하다 **it that** no one besides me noticed him! Everyone should have looked at him, everyone should have trembled! But no one heeded him. He sat there like a statue 조각상, and, I thought, proud as an idol! A fly lighted on his forehead and scurried across his nose and lips -- not a muscle twitched 움직이다. Where was he now? What was he thinking? What did he feel? Was he in heaven or was he in hell?

I was unable to put a question to him. At the end of the period, when I saw him alive and breathing again, as

carved 조각된
uniformly pale
균일하게 창백한

the part ~ **that** seemed
가장 살아있는 듯한 그의 일부

limp 맥없이 늘어진
pods sheathing
~를 감싸고 있는 꼬투리

대명사 **that**: 그의 말과 행동은
someone **who** plays, adapts, and does ~하는 사람
out of sheer complaisance
순전히 친절함에서
as ~하듯이, ~처럼
primeval 태고의, 원시의
marble 냉혹한, 무정한
fabulous 멋진, 전설적인

ether 공기, 분위기

go completely into himself
완전히 자신 속으로 침잠하다

부정부사 도치구조
=I had never been

가정법 과거완료:
그가 세상에서 가장 먼 섬에 있는 것보다 더 멀리 있다

가목적어 **it**, 진목적어 **that**

should have -pp:
~했어야 했는데
heed=pay attention to

scurry=move quickly

his glance met mine, he was the same as he had been before. Where did he come from? Where had he been? He seemed tired. His face was no longer pale, his hands moved again, but now the brown hair was without luster 윤기, as though lifeless.

During the next few days, I began a new exercise in my bedroom. I would sit rigid in a chair, make my eyes rigid too, and stay completely motionless and see how long I could keep it up, and what I would feel. I only felt very tired and my eyelids itched.

would sit rigid
꼼짝 않고 앉아 있곤 했다

간접의문문: 의문사+주어+동사
how long I could keep ~
what I would feel

Shortly afterwards we were confirmed, an event that calls forth no important memories whatever.

be confirmed
견진성사를 받다
an event 견진성사
call forth=arouse
불러일으키다

Now everything changed. My childhood world was breaking apart around me. My parents eyed me with a certain embarrassment 곤혹. My sisters had become strangers to me. A disenchantment 각성 falsified and blunted my usual feelings and joys: the garden lacked fragrance 향기, the woods held no attraction for me, the world stood around me like a clearance sale of last year's secondhand goods, insipid, all its charm gone. Books were so much paper, music a grating noise. That is the way leaves fall around a tree in autumn, a tree unaware of the rain running down its sides, of the sun or the frost, and of life gradually retreating inward. The tree does not die. It waits.

falsify 거짓으로 만들다

blunt 무디게 하다

insipid=dull 무미건조한

grating 귀에 거슬리는

gradually retreat inward
점차 내부로 후퇴하다

It had been decided **that** I would be sent away to a boarding school at the end of the vacation; for the first time I would be away from home. Sometimes my mother approached me with particular tenderness, **as if** already taking leave of me ahead of time, **intent on** inspiring love, homesickness, the unforgettable in my heart. Demian was away on a trip. I was alone.

가주어 it, 진주어 that

접속사 (주어+be) 생략:
as if (she was) already
마치 미리 작별을 고하는
것처럼
분사구 (being) intent on
~을 심어주고자 애쓰며

Chapter IV
Beatrice

IV. Beatrice

베아트리체: 단테의 사랑과
시혼의 원천이 되었던
여성이기도 하다.

At the end of the holidays, and without having seen my friend again, I went to St.___. My parents accompanied 동반하다 me and entrusted 맡기다 me to the care of a boy's boarding-house run by one of the teachers at the preparatory school. They would have been struck dumb with horror **had they known** into what world they were letting me wander.

run by ~dp 의해 운영되는

preparatory school
대학입학 준비학교
가정법 과거완료
=if they had known ~
사역동사+목+목/보(동):
let me wander

The question remained: was I eventually to become a good son and useful citizen or did my nature 천성 point in an altogether different direction? My last attempt to achieve happiness in the shadow of the paternal home had lasted a long time, had on occasion almost succeeded, but had completely failed in the end.

point in ~ direction
전혀 다른 방향으로 나아가다

paternal 아버지의

on occasion=sometimes

The peculiar emptiness and isolation 고독 that I came to feel for the first time after Confirmation (oh, how familiar **it** was to become afterwards, this desolate, thin air!) passed only very slowly. My leave-taking 작별 from home was surprisingly easy, I was almost ashamed that I did not feel more nostalgic. My sisters wept for no reason; my eyes remained dry. I was astonished at myself. I had always been an emotional and essentially good child. Now I had completely changed. I behaved with utter indifference to the world outside and for days on end voices within preoccupied 사로잡다 me, inner streams, the forbidden dark streams that roared below the surface. I had grown several inches in the last half year and I walked lanky and half-finished through the world. I had lost any charm I might ever have had and felt that no one could possibly love me the way I was. I certainly had no love for myself. Often I felt a great longing for Max Demian, but no less often I hated him,

대명사 it=this desolate,
thin air 이 공허하고 희박한
공기가 나중에 얼마나 친숙해
졌는가!

nostalgic 향수를 느끼는

essentially 본질적으로

utter=sheer 완전한
indifference 무관심, 냉담
for days on end
며칠이나 계속하여

멀대 같이 길고 완성되지
않은 팔다리로 세상을
활개치고 다니다

the way I was
있는 그대로의 나의 모습으로

no less 역시:
놀람이나 감탄을 나타냄

accusing him of having caused the impoverishment 빈곤 of my life that held me in its sway like a foul disease.

I was neither liked nor respected in my boys' boarding-house. I was teased to begin with, then avoided and looked upon as a sneak 겁쟁이 and an unwelcome oddity 괴짜. I fell in with this role, even exaggerated 과장하다 it, and grumbled myself into a self-isolation 자기고독 that must have appeared to outsiders like permanent and masculine contempt 사내다운 경멸 of the world, whereas, in truth, I often secretly succumbed to consuming fits 통절한 발작 of melancholy and despair. In school I managed to get by on the knowledge accumulated 축적된 in my previous class — the present one lagged somewhat behind the one I had left — and I began to regard the students in my age group contemptuously 경멸적으로 as mere children.

It went on like this for a year or more. The first few visits back home left me cold. I was glad when I could leave again. It was the beginning of November. I had become used to taking short meditative walks during all kinds of weather, walks on which I often enjoyed a kind of rapture tinged with melancholy 우울, scorn 냉소 of the world and self-hatred 자기혐오. Thus I roamed 배회하다 in the foggy dusk one evening through the town. The broad avenue 가로수길 of a public park stood deserted 황량한, **beckoning** me to enter; the path lay thickly carpeted with fallen leaves which I stirred angrily with my feet. There was a damp 축축한, bitter smell, and distant trees, shadowy as ghosts, loomed huge out of the mist 안개.

I stopped irresolute at the far end of the avenue: **staring** into the dark foliage 무성한 잎 I greedily breathed the humid fragrance 향기 of decay and dying **to which** something within me responded with greeting.

accuse A of B:
B에 대해서 A를 비난하다
hold me in its sway like ~
내 삶의 빈곤이 더러운
질병처럼 나를 지배하다

be teased 괴롭힘을 당하다
to begin with 처음에는
be looked upon as
~로 간주되다
fall in with this role
이 역할을 받아들이다
grumble me into ~
투덜거리며 ~속으로 빠져들다
must have appeared like ~
~처럼 보여 졌음에 틀림없다
succumb to ~에 굴복하다

manage to get by on
~로 그럭저럭 살아가다
=knowledge (which was)
accumulated
one=class 수업, 반

be used to=be accustomed
to ~ing ~에 익숙하다
meditative walks
명상을 하며 걷는 산책

rapture (which was) tinged
with ~에 물든 환희

in the foggy dusk
안개 자욱한 해질 무렵에
stand deserted
인적 없이/황량하게 서 있다
분사구 beckoning:
~하라고 손짓하면서

loom huge 거대한 모습을
어렴풋이 드러내다
stop irresolute(ly)
망설이며 멈추어 서다
분사구 staring into:
~를 응시하면서
to which ~ respond
~가 부패와 죽음의 축축한
향기에 반응하다

Someone stepped out of one of the side paths, **his coat billowing** as he walked — I was about to continue when a voice called out.

"Hello, Sinclair."

He came up to me. It was Alfons Beck, the oldest boy in our boardinghouse. I was always glad to see him, had nothing against him **except that** he treated me, and all others who were younger, with an element of ironic and avuncular condescension. He was reputed to be strong as a bear and to have the teacher in our house completely under his thumb. He was the hero of many a student rumor.

"Well, what are you doing here?" he called out affably 상냥하게 in that tone the bigger boys affected when they occasionally condescended to talk to one of us. "I'll bet anything you're making a poem."

"Wouldn't think of it," I replied brusquely 퉁명스럽게. He laughed out loud, walked beside me, and made small talk in a way I hadn't been used to for a long time.

"You don't need to be afraid that I wouldn't understand, Sinclair. There's something to walking with autumnal thoughts through the evening fog. One likes to compose poems at a time like that, I know. About moribund nature, of course, and one's lost youth, which resembles **it**. Heinrich Heine, for example."

"I'm not as sentimental as all that," I defended myself.

"All right, let's drop the subject. But it seems to me that in weather like this a man does the right thing when he looks for a quiet place **where** he can drink a good glass of wine or something. Will you join me? I happen to be all by myself at the moment. Or would you rather not? I don't want to be the one who leads you astray, mon vieux, that is, **in case** you happen to be the

---

주어+분사구(billowing):
그의 코트를 휘날리며

continue (walking)
when=and then 그때

접속사 except that:
~를 제외하고
treat A with B: 빈정대고
삼촌과 같은 거들먹거리는
태도로 나를 다루었다.
reputed=well-known
have ~ under one's thumb
~를 꼼짝 못하게 하다
many a rumor is
=many rumors are

affect ~인체 하다

condescend to
체면을 버리고 겸손하게 ~하다
bet A (that) B: B에 A를 걸다

there is something to ~ing
~하는 데는 뭔가가 있다

moribund nature
죽어가는, 소멸해가는 자연
it=moribund nature
Heinrich Heine
하이네, 독일시인

drop the subject
그런 이야기 집어 치우자

관계부사 where

lead A astray
A를 그릇된 길로 인도하다
mon vieux 형씨: 가깝지 않은
상대를 부를 때
in case ~할 경우에 대비해서

kind that keeps to the straight and narrow."

Soon afterwards we were sitting in a small dive 술집 at the edge of town, **drinking** a wine of doubtful quality and **clinking** the thick glasses. I didn't much like it to begin with, but at least it was something new. Soon, however, unused to the wine, I became very loquacious 수다스러운.

It was as though an interior window had opened **through which** the world sparkled. For how long, for how terribly long hadn't I really talked to anyone? My imagination began to run away with me and eventually I even popped out with the story of Cain and Abel.

Beck listened with evident pleasure — finally here was someone **to whom** I was able to give something! He patted me on the shoulder, called me one hell of a fellow, and my heart swelled ecstatically 황홀하게 at this opportunity to luxuriate in the release of a long pent-up need for talk and communication, for acknowledgment 인정 from an older boy. When he called me a damned clever little bastard 녀석, the words ran like sweet wine into my soul. The world glowed 타오르다 in new colors, thoughts gushed out of a hundred audacious springs. The fire of enthusiasm 열광 flared up within me. We discussed our teachers and fellow students and it seemed to me that we understood each other perfectly. We talked about the Greeks and the pagans 이교도 in general and Beck very much wanted me to confess to having slept with girls. This was out of my league. I hadn't experienced anything, certainly nothing worth telling. And what I had felt, what I had constructed 구성하다 in imagination, ached within me but had not been loosened or made communicable by the wine. Beck knew much more about girls, so I listened to his exploits 영웅담 without being able to say a word. I heard incredible

keep to the straight and narrow 곧고 좁은 길을 고수하다 (모범생의 길을 가다)

분사구 drinking, clinking: 술을 마시고 잔을 부딪치면서

(being) unused to ~에 익숙하지 않아서

pop out with the story of 갑자기 ~ 이야기를 꺼내다

one hell of a fellow 대단한 놈, 녀석

luxuriate in ~을 즐기다
pent-up=depressed
pent-up need 억압된 욕구

damned 놀라운, 빌어먹을

gush out of
~에서 뿜어져 나오다
audacious springs 대담한 샘

out of my league (범주)
나에게 너무 과하다

ache within me
내 안에서 간절히 바라다

ben loosened or made communicable by thw wine 술기운에 의해 느슨해지거나 말로 전달되지는 않았다

things. Things I had never thought possible became everyday reality, seemed normal. Alfons Beck, who was eighteen, seemed to be able to draw on a vast body of experience. For instance, he had learned that it was a funny thing about girls, they just wanted to flirt 희롱하다, which was all very well, but not the real thing. For the real thing one could hope for greater success with women. Women were much more reasonable. Mrs. Jaggelt, for example, who owned the stationery store 문방구, well, with her one could talk business, and all the things that had happened behind her counter wouldn't fit into a book.

I sat there enchanted and also dumbfounded. Certainly, I could never have loved Mrs. Jaggelt — yet the news was incredible. There seemed to be hidden sources of pleasure 쾌감의 원천, at least for the older boys, of which I had not even dreamed. Something about it didn't sound right, and it tasted less appealing 흥미를 끄는 and more ordinary than love, I felt, was supposed to taste — but at least: this was reality, this was life and adventure, and next to me sat someone who had experienced it, to whom it seemed normal.

Once it had reached this height, our conversation began to taper off. I was no longer the damned clever little bastard; I'd shrunk to a mere boy listening to a man. Yet all the same — compared with what my life had been for months — this was delicious, this was paradise. Besides, it was, as I began to realize only gradually, very much prohibited 금지된 from our presence in the bar to the subject of our talk. At least for me it smacked of rebellion.

I can remember that night with remarkable clarity. We started on our way home through the damp, past gas

draw on a vast body of experience 방대한 경험을 펼치다

flirt with ~와 희롱하다

women 소녀가 아니라 부인들

not fit into a book 책에 적기에는 부적절하다

enchanted 마법에 걸린
dumbfounded
놀라서 말문이 막힌

it=our conversation

taper off 점점 줄다
=gradually diminish
shrink to ~로 움츠러들다
shrink-shrank-shrunk

besides =in addition
접속사 as: ~하듯
from A to B: A에서 B에 이르기까지

smack of rebellion
반란의 맛/기미가 있다

with clarity 분명하게

- 81 -

lamps dimly **lighting** the late night: for the first time in my life I was drunk. It was not pleasant. In fact it was most painful, yet it had something, a thrill, a sweetness of rebellious orgy, that was life and spirit. Beck did a good job taking charge of me, even though he cursed me bitterly as a "bloody beginner," 순전한 초짜 and half led, half carried me home. There he succeeded in smuggling me through an open window in the hallway.

The sober reality **to which** I awoke after a brief deathlike sleep coincided with a painful and senseless depression 우울. I sat up in bed, still wearing my shirt. The rest of my clothes, **strewn** *about* on the floor, reeked of tobacco and vomit 구토. Between fits 발작 of headache, nausea 메스꺼움, and a raging thirst an image came to mind **which** I had not viewed for a long time: I visualized my parents' house, my home, my father and mother, my sisters, the garden. I could see the familiar bedroom, the school, the market place, could see Demian and the Confirmation 견진성사 classes — everything was wonderful, godly pure, and everything, all of this -as I realized now — had still been mine yesterday, a few hours ago, had waited for me; yet now, at this very hour, everything looked ravaged 황폐한 and damned 저주받은, was mine no longer, rejected me, regarded me with disgust 혐오. Everything dear and intimate, everything my parents had given me as far back as the distant gardens of my childhood, every kiss from my mother, every Christmas, each devout, light-filled Sunday morning at home, each and every flower in the garden — everything had been laid waste, everything had been trampled on by me! If the arm of the law **had reached** out for me now, **had bound and gagged** me and led me to the gallows 교수대 as the scum of the earth and a desecrator of the

분사구 lighting:
희미하게 ~를 비추는

rebellious orgy
반항적인 방탕, 탐닉

smuggle A through B:
B를 통해 몰래 A를 데리고
들어오다

sober 술 취하지 않는, 온건한
the sober reality to which
awoke 잠에서 깨어 깨달은
냉혹한 현실
coincide with ~와 일치하다

분사구 (being) strewn:
strew-strewed-strewn
~주위에 흩어져 있는
reek of=smell of
raging thirst 극심한 갈증
an image **which** I had not

visualize ~를 마음에 그리다

lay A waste: A를 초토화하다
be laid waste 초토화되다
waste=deserted, useless
be trampled on
짓밟아 뭉개지다
가정법 과거완료:
만약 ~했더라면, ~했을 텐데
gag 재갈을 물리다

temple, I **would not have objected**, would have gladly gone, would have considered it just and fair.

So that's what I looked like inside! I who was going about contemptuous of the world! I who was proud in spirit and shared Demian's thoughts! That's what I looked like, a piece of excrement 배설물, a filthy swine, drunk and filthy, loathsome and callow, a vile beast brought low by hideous appetites. **That's** what I looked like, **I, who** came out of such pure gardens where everything was cleanliness, radiance, and tenderness, **I, who** had loved the music of Bach and beautiful poetry.

With nausea and outrage 분노 I could still hear my life, drunk and unruly 제멋대로의, **sputtering** out of me in idiotic laughter, in jerks and fits. There I was. In spite of everything, I almost reveled in my agonies 고뇌. I had been blind and insensible and my heart had been silent for **so** long, had cowered impoverished in a corner, **that** even this self-accusation 자책감, this dread, all these horrible feelings were welcome. At least it was feeling of some kind, at least there were some flames, the heart at least flickered 깜빡거리다. Confusedly I felt something like liberation 해방 amid my misery 불행.

Meanwhile, **viewed** from the outside, I was going rapidly downhill. My first drunken frenzy 광란 was soon followed by others. There was much going to bars and carousing in our school. I was one of the youngest to take part, yet soon enough I was not merely a fledgling 풋내기 **whom** one grudgingly 마지못해 took along, I had become the ringleader and star, a notorious and daring bar crawler. Once again I belonged entirely to the world of darkness and to the devil, and in this world I had the reputation 명성 of being one hell of a fellow.

Nonetheless, I felt wretched 비참한. I lived in an orgy of

scum 인간쓰레기, 불량배
desecrator 훼손한 자
object 반감을 품다

go about contemptuous of
~를 경멸하며 돌아다니다

filthy swine 더러운 돼지
loathsome 역겨운
callow 풋내기의
a vile beast (which was) brought low by ~
섬뜩한 욕구에 의해서 타락한 비열한 짐승
그것이 바로 나의 모습이었다.
That's I who came out ~
그것이 바로 나였다.

지각동사+목적어+목적보어:
hear my life sputtering ~
나의 삶이 지껄여 대는 소리를 듣다
in idiotic laughter, in jerks and fits
바보 같은 웃음과 발작 속에서
revel in ~에 빠지다

so ~ that 구조
그토록 오래 내가 구석에서 힘없이 웅크리고 있었기에
cower impoverished
비참함으로 위축되다

go downhill 내리막길을 걷다
분사구 viewed
=if I was viewed from

carouse 술잔치, 흥청거림

목적격 관계대명사 whom:
사람들이 마지못해 데리고 다니는 풋내기
ringleader 주모자, 장본인
bar crawler 이 술집 저 술집을 옮겨 다니는 자

one hell of a man
굉장한 놈
live in an gory of
기를 쓰고 ~하며 살다

self-destruction 자기파괴 and, while my friends regarded me as a leader and as a damned sharp and funny fellow, deep down inside me my soul grieved 비탄에 젖다. I can still remember tears springing to my eyes when I saw children playing in the street on Sunday morning as I emerged from a bar, children with freshly combed hair and dressed in their Sunday best. Those friends who sat with me in the lowest dives 저렴한 술집 among beer puddles 흘린 맥주 and dirty tables I amused 즐겁게 하다 with remarks of unprecedented cynicism, often even shocked them; yet in my inmost heart I was in awe of everything I belittled and lay weeping before my soul, my past, my mother, before God.

There was good reason **why** I never became one with my companions 동료, **why** I felt alone among them and was therefore able to suffer so much. I was a barroom hero and cynic 냉소주의자 to satisfy the taste of the most brutal. I displayed wit and courage in my ideas and remarks about teachers, school, parents, and church. I could also bear 견디다 to hear the filthiest stories and even ventured an occasional one myself, but I never accompanied my friends when they visited women. I was alone and was filled with intense longing for love, a hopeless longing, while, to judge by my talk, I should have been a hard-boiled sensualist 비정한 향락주의자. No one was more easily hurt, no one more bashful than I. And when I happened to see the young well-brought-up girls of the town walking in front of me, pretty and clean, innocent and graceful, they seemed like wonderful pure dreams, a thousand times too good for me.

For a time I could not even bring myself to enter Mrs. Jaggelt's stationery store because I blushed looking at her **remembering** what Alfons Beck had told me.

---

sharp 예리한, 신랄한

emerge from=come from

목적어도치: 목+주+동
=I amused those ~ tables

목적어 도치구조:
I amused (those friends who ~ dirty tables)
with remarks of unprecedented cynicism
전례 없는 냉소적인 말로
be in awe of ~를 경외하다:
belittle 하찮게 생각하다
lie weeping before
~ 앞에서 엎드려 흐느끼다
관계부사 **why**: ~한 이유

venture an occasional one
가끔은 나도 그런 추잡한 이야기를 하기도 한다.
to judge by my talk
내가 하는 이야기로 나를 판단하면
should have pp
~로 여겼을 것이다

지각동사+목+목/보(~ing):
see ~ walking

분사구 remembering:
~를 기억하면서

The more I realized that I was to remain perpetually lonely and different within my new group of friends **the less** I was able to break away. I really don't know any longer whether boozing and swaggering actually ever gave me any pleasure. Moreover, I never became **so** used to drinking **that** I did not always feel embarrassing after-effects. It was all **as if** I were somehow under a compulsion 충동 to do these things. I simply did what I had to do, because I had no idea what to do with myself otherwise. I was afraid of being alone for long, was afraid of the many tender and chaste 정숙한 moods that would overcome 압도하다 me, was afraid of the thoughts of love surging up in me.

What I missed above all else was a friend. There were two or three fellow students whom I could have cared for, but they were in good standing and my vices had long been an open secret. They avoided me. I was regarded by and large as a hopeless rebel **whose** ground was slipping from under his feet. The teachers were well-informed about me, I had been severely punished several times, my final expulsion 제적 seemed merely a matter of time. I realized myself that I had become a poor student, but I wriggled strenuously through one exam after the other, always feeling that it couldn't go on like this much longer.

There are numerous ways **in which** God can make us lonely and lead us back to ourselves. This was **the way** He dealt with me at that time. It was like a bad dream. I can see myself: crawling along in my odious 혐오할 and unclean way, across filth and slime, across broken beer glasses and through cynically wasted nights, a spellbound dreamer, restless and racked 고통 받는. There are dreams in which on your way to the princess you become stuck

the 비교급, the 비교급

boozing 술을 마시고
swaggering 허풍을 떨어대는 짓

be used to ~에 익숙하다
숙취를 느끼지 않을 만큼 술에
익숙하지는 않았다

surge up in me
나에게로 갑자기 밀려들다
above all else
다른 무엇보다도

be in good standing
착실한

by and large=generally 대개
be regarded as ~로 간주되다
소유격 관/대 whose: 중심이
흔들리는 희망이 없는 문제아

wriggle strenuously
격렬하게 몸부림치다

in which=where
the way how (x)
the way=how ~하는 방법

see myself crawling

filth and slime
오물과 악취 나는 점액
cynically wasted nights
냉소적으로 떠벌리며 낭비된 밤

become stuck in
~속에 갇히다

in quagmires 진흙탕, in back alleys full of foul odors 악취 and refuse 오물. That was how it was with me. In this unpleasant fashion I was condemned to become lonely, and I raised between myself and my childhood a locked gateway to Eden with its pitilessly resplendent host of guardians. It was a beginning, an awakening of nostalgia 향수 for my former self.

Yet I had not become so callous 무감각한 as not to be startled into twinges of fear when my father, alarmed by my tutor's letters, appeared for the first time in St. ___ and confronted me unexpectedly. Later on that winter, when he came a second time, nothing could move me any more, I let him scold and entreat 간청하다 me, let him remind me of my mother. Finally toward the end of the meeting he became quite angry and said if I didn't change he would have me expelled from the school in disgrace 치욕 and placed in a reformatory. Well, let him!

When he went away that time I felt sorry for him; he had accomplished nothing, he had not found a way to me ─ and at moments I felt that it served him right.

I could not have cared less what became of me. In my odd and unattractive fashion, going to bars and bragging 허풍 was my way of quarreling with the world ─ this was my way of protesting. I was ruining myself in the process but at times I understood the situation as follows: if the world had no use for people like me, if it did not have a better place and higher tasks for them, well, in that case, people like me would go to pot, and the loss would be the world's.

Christmas vacation was a joyless affair that year. My mother was deeply startled when she saw me. I had shot up even more and my lean 야윈 face looked gray and wasted 쇠약한, with slack features and inflamed eyes. The

be condemned to =be destined to ~할 운명이다
raise a locked gateway to 무자비하게 (눈을) 번득이는 파수꾼이 지키는 에덴으로 가는 잠긴 문을 세우다

not so A as not to ~하지 않을 만큼 A하지 않다
be startled in twinges of fear 놀라서 기겁을 하다

confront=faced 직면하다

사역동사+목+목/보(동):
let ~ scold and entreat
let ~ remind me of

사역동사+목+목/보(pp):
have A expelled from ~로부터 퇴학당하게 만들다
reformatory 감화원, 소년원

accomplish=achieved 성취하다
at moments=sometimes
it serves him right 그런 일이 그에게 합당하다
~ what became of me 내가 어떤 인간이 되어도 상관이 없었다.

go to pot=be destroyed

shoot up 쑥 자라다
shoot-shot-shot

slack 축 늘어진
inflamed eyes 충혈 된 눈

first touch of a mustache 콧수염 and the eyeglasses I had just begun wearing made me look odder still. My sisters shied away and giggled. Everything was most unedifying. Disagreeable and bitter was the talk I had with my father in his study, disagreeable exchanging greetings with a handful of relatives, and particularly unpleasant was Christmas Eve itself. Ever since I had been a little child this had been the great day in our house. The evening was a festivity of love and gratitude 감사, **when** the bond between child and parents was renewed. This time everything was merely oppressive and embarrassing. As usual my father read aloud the passage about the shepherds 양치기 in the fields "watching their flocks," as usual my sisters stood radiantly before a table decked with gifts, but father's voice sounded disgruntled 언짢은, his face looked old and strained, and mother was sad. Everything seemed out of place: the presents and Christmas greetings, Gospel reading and the lit-up tree. The gingerbread smelled sweet; it exuded 발산하다 a host of memories which were even sweeter. The fragrance 향기 of the Christmas tree told of a world that no longer existed. I longed for evening and for the holidays to be over.

It went on like this the entire winter. Only a short while back I had been given a stern warning 엄중한 경고 by the teachers' council and been threatened with expulsion. It couldn't go on much longer. Well, I didn't care.

I held a very special grudge 원한 against Max Demian, whom I hadn't seen again even once. I had written him twice during my first months in St. ___ but had received no reply; so I had not called on him during the holidays.

In the same park in which I had met Alfons Beck in the fall, a girl came to my attention in early spring **as** the thorn hedges began to bud. I had taken a walk by

사역동사+목+목/보(동):
made ~ look odder

shy away 꽁무니를 빼다
giggle 키들거리다
unedifying 교화적이지 못한
보어 도치 구문: 보어+동+주
=the talk (I had ~ study)
was disagreeable and bitter
disagreeable 유쾌하지 못한
=Christmas Eve itself was
particularly unpleasant.

this=Christmas Eve

festivity 축제의 행사/기분
관계부사 **when**=and then

radiantly 밝게, 환하게
decked with ~로 꾸며진

light-lit-lit 불 켜진 나무

a host of=a lot of

only a short while back
바로 얼마 전에

expulsion 제적, 퇴학

call on==visit

접속사 **as**=when

thorn hedges 가시 울타리

myself, my head filled with vile thoughts and worries —
for my health had deteriorated 악화되다 — and to make
matters worse I was perpetually 지속적으로 in financial
difficulties, owed 빚지다 friends considerable sums and had
thus continually to invent expenditures so as to receive
money from home. In a number of stores I had allowed
bills to mount for cigars and similar things. **Not that** this
worried me much. If my existence was about to come to
a sudden end anyway — if I drowned myself or was sent
to the reformatory — a few small extras didn't make
much difference. Yet I was forced to live face to face
with these unpleasant details: they made me wretched.

On that spring day in the park I saw a young woman
who attracted me. She was tall and slender, elegantly
dressed, and had an intelligent and boyish face. I liked
her at once. She was my type and began to fill my
imagination. She probably was not much older than I but
seemed far more mature, well-defined, a full-grown
woman, but with a touch 느낌 of exuberance and
boyishness in her face, and this was what I liked above
all.

I had never managed to approach a girl **with whom** I
had fallen in love, nor did I manage in this case. But the
impression 인상 she made on me was deeper than any
previous one had been and the infatuation 심취 had a
profound influence on my life.

Suddenly a new image had risen up before me, a lofty
and cherished 소중한 image. And no need, no urge was **as**
deep or **as** fervent 격렬한 within me **as** the craving 갈망 to
worship and admire. I gave her the name Beatrice, for,
even though I had not read Dante, I knew about Beatrice
from an English painting of which I owned a reproduction
복제품. It showed a young pre-Raphaelite woman,

to make matters worse
설상가상으로

invent expenditures
지출명목을 꾸며내다

mount=increase
not that ~라는 말은 아니다
come to an end 끝나다

사역동사+목+목/보(pp):
made me wretched
나를 비참하게 만들다

well-defined 윤곽이 뚜렷한

exuberance 풍부, 성숙

fall in love with

부정어 도치구조:
nor *did I manage*
impression (**that**) she made
one=impression

as A or as B as C:
C만큼 A하거나 B하지 않다

베아트리체: '신곡'에 묘사된
단테가 사랑하여 이상화한 여성

long-limbed and slender, with long head and etherealized   etherealized=angel-like
hands and features. My beautiful young woman did not
quite resemble her, even though she, too, revealed that
slender and boyish figure which I loved, and something
of the ethereal, soulful quality of her face.

Although I never addressed a single word to Beatrice,
she exerted 발휘하다 a profound influence on me at that
time. She raised her image before me, she gave me
access to a holy shrine, she transformed me into a   shrine=divine place 성소
worshiper in a temple.   transform A into B:
                                                          A를 B로 변형시키다

From one day to the next I stayed clear of all bars   stay clear of ~와 멀어지다
and nocturnal exploits. I could be alone with myself   nocturnal exploits
again and enjoyed reading and going for long walks.   밤의 활동들

My sudden conversion 변화 drew a good deal of mockery
조롱 in its wake. But now I had something I loved and   in its wake 처음에는
venerated 존경하다, I had an ideal again, life was rich with   =in the beginning
                                                          venerated=respected
intimations of mystery and a feeling of dawn **that** made   **관계사 that**: 내가 모든
                                                          비웃음에 무감각해지도록
me immune to all taunts. I had come home again to   만드는 ~ 느낌
myself, even if only as the slave and servant of a   even if only as:
cherished 소중한 image.   비록 ~로서 이지만

I find it difficult to think back to that time without a
certain fondness. Once more I was trying most
strenuously to construct an intimate "world of light" for
myself out of the shambles of a period of devastation;   shambles 비틀거림
once more I sacrificed everything within me to the aim   devastation 황폐
                                                          sacrifice A to B:
of banishing 추방하다 darkness and evil from myself. And,   A를 B에 바치다/희생하다
furthermore, this present "world of light" was to some
extent my own creation; it was no longer an escape, no   to some extent
                                                          어느 정도 까지는
crawling back to mother and the safety of irresponsibility;
it was a new duty, one I had invented and desired on   one (**that**) I had invented
my own, with responsibility and self-control. My   on my own 내 스스로
sexuality, a torment **from which** I was in constant flight,   내가 계속 달아나려고 했던 고뇌
was to be transfigured into spirituality and devotion by   be transfigured into
                                                          =be transformed into

this holy fire. Everything dark and hateful was to be banished, there were to be no more tortured nights, no excitement before lascivious 음란한 pictures, no eavesdropping 엿듣기 at forbidden doors, no lust. In place of all this I raised my altar to the image of Beatrice, and by consecrating myself to her I consecrated myself to the spirit and to the gods, **sacrificing** that part of life which I withdrew from the forces of ·darkness **to** those of light. My goal was not joy but purity 순수, not happiness but beauty, and spirituality 영성.

This cult 숭배 of Beatrice completely changed my life. Yesterday a precocious cynic 조숙한 냉소가, today I was an acolyte **whose** aim was to become a saint. I not only avoided the bad life **to which** I had become accustomed, I sought to transform myself by introducing purity and nobility into every aspect of my life. In this connection I thought of my eating and drinking habits, my language and dress. I began my mornings with cold baths which cost me a great effort at first. My behavior became serious and dignified 품위 있는; I carried myself stiffly and assumed a slow and dignified 품위 있는 gait. It may have looked comic to outsiders but to me it was a genuine act of worship.

Of all the new practices **in which** I sought to express my new conviction 확신, one became truly important to me. I began to paint. The starting point for this was **that** the reproduction 복제품 of the English picture I owned did not resemble my Beatrice closely enough. I wanted to try to paint her portrait 초상화 for myself. With new joy and hopefulness I bought beautiful paper, paints, and brushes and carried them to my room — I had just been given one of my own — and prepared my palette, glass, porcelain dishes 도자기 접시 and pencils. The delicate

everything (**which was**) dark and hateful

in place of ~대신에

altar to ~를 기리는 제단
consecrate A to B: A를 B에 바치다

분사구 sacrificing A to B: 어두운 힘에서 되찾은 내 삶의 일부를 빛의 힘에게 바치면서 those=forces

acolyte=altar boy: 미사의 시중을 드는 소년(복사)
whose=and his aim
be accustomed to ~~에 익숙하다

in this connection 이와 관련하여

carry myself stiffly 자세를 똑바로 하다
assume ~ gait ~한 걸음걸이를 취하다
may have looked ~ ~하게 보였을지도 모른다

in which 새로운 연습 속에서

was that: ~하다는 것 이었다

내가 혼자 사용하도록 최근에 주어진 된 나의 방

고운 템페라 물감

tempera colors in the little tubes I had bought delighted me. Among them was a fiery chrome green **that**, I think, I can still see today **as** it flashed up for the first time in the small white dish.

I began with great care. Painting the likeness of a face was difficult. I wanted to try myself out first on something else. I painted ornaments 장식, flowers, small imagined landscapes 풍경: a tree by a chapel 예배당, a Roman bridge with cypress trees. Sometimes I became **so** completely immersed in this game **that** I was as happy as a little child with his paintbox. Finally I set out on my portrait of Beatrice.

A few attempts failed completely and I discarded them. **The more** I sought to imagine the face of the girl I had encountered 만나다 here and there on the street **the less** successful I was. Finally I gave up the attempt 시도 and contented myself with giving in to my imagination and intuition **that** arose spontaneously from the first strokes, as though out of the paint and brush themselves. **It was** a dream face **that** emerged and I was not dissatisfied with it. Yet I persisted and every new sketch was more distinct, approximated more nearly the type I desired, even if it in no way reproduced reality.

I grew more and more accustomed to idly drawing lines with a dreaming paintbrush and to coloring areas **for which** I had no model in mind, that were the result of playful fumblings of my subconscious 무의식. Finally, one day I produced, almost without knowing it, a face **to which** I responded more strongly than I had **to** any of the others. It was not the face of that girl — it wasn't supposed to be that any longer. It was something else, something unreal, yet it was no less valuable to me. It looked more like a boy's face than a girl's, the hair was

---

목적격 관/대 (that) 생략
=tubes (that) I had bought green that I can still see

접속사 as: ~한 모습 그대로
flash up 빛나다, 타오르다
it=the fiery chrome green
빛나는 초록색 물감

처음에는 뭔가 다른 것을 시도해 보려고 했다.

so ~ that 구조

be immersed in ~에 몰입하다

set out on=began

discard 버리다

the 비교급, the 비교급

content myself with
=be satisfied with
give in to ~에 굴복하다
arise spontaneously
자발적으로 생기다
arise-arose-arisen
strokes 붓질
It was ~ that 강조 구문:
그 결과 그려진 것은 내가 꿈꾸던 얼굴 이었다
emerge=appear
approximate ~에 가까워지다
in no way=never
결코 현실적인 모습은 아니다
grow(=be) accustomed to

have a model for
~에 대한 모델이 있다
playful fumblings
장난스러운 어설픈 짓
respond to ~에 반응하다
생략구조=I had (responded) to any of the others
be supposed to
~인 것으로 여겨지다

that=a face of that girl

not flaxen like **that** of my pretty girl, but dark brown with a reddish hue 색조. The chin was strong and determined 단호한, the mouth **like** a red flower. As a whole it was somewhat stiff 경직된 and mask-like but it was impressive and full of a secret life of its own.

As I sat down in front of the completed painting, it had an odd effect on me. It resembled a kind of image of God or a holy mask, half male, half female, ageless, as purposeful as it was dreamy, as rigid as it was secretly alive. This face seemed to have a message for me, it belonged to me, it was asking something of me. It bore a resemblance to someone, yet I did not know whom.

For a time this portrait haunted 사로잡다 my thoughts and shared my life. I kept it locked in a drawer **so that** no one would take it and taunt 비웃다 me with it. But as soon as I was alone in my small room I took it out and communed with it. In the evening I pinned it on the wall **facing** my bed and gazed on it until I fell asleep and in the morning it was the first thing my eyes opened on.

It was precisely at this time **that** I again began having many dreams, **as** I had always had **as** a child. It felt as though I had not dreamed for years. Now the dreams returned with entirely new images, and time after time the portrait appeared among them, alive and eloquent, friendly or hostile to me, sometimes distorted into a grimace, sometimes infinitely beautiful, harmonious, and noble.

Then one morning, as I awoke from one of these dreams, I suddenly recognized it. It looked at me **as though** it **were** fabulously familiar and seemed to call out my name. It seemed to know who I was, like a mother, **as if** its eyes **had been fixed** on me since the beginning

---

flaxen=blonde 금발의
that=the hair

생략=the mouth (was) like

as a whole 전체적으로 볼 때

have an odd effect on me
나에게 묘한 영향을 미치다

as ~ alive: 몽상적이지만 의미심장하고, 은밀하게 살아 움직이지만 경직된

bear a resemblance to
=resemble ~와 닮아 있다

접속사 so that: 그래서

commune with ~와 소통하다

분사구 facing my bed:
나의 침대와 마주 보도록

It ~ that 강조 구문

접속사 as: ~하듯이
전치사 as: ~로서

eloquent 생생한, 풍부한

distort into a grimace
찡그린 얼굴로 왜곡되다

as if 가정법: 마치 ~인 것처럼
fabulously familiar
믿기 어려울 만치 친숙한
as if 가정법과거완료:
마치 ~이었던 것처럼

of time. With a quivering 떨리는 heart I stared at the sheet, the close brown hair, the half-feminine mouth, the pronounced forehead with the strange brightness (**it** had dried this way of its own accord) and I felt myself coming nearer and nearer to the recognition, the rediscovery, the knowledge.

I leapt out of bed, stepped up to the face, and from inches away looked into its wide-open, greenish, rigid eyes, the right one slightly higher than the left. All at once the right eye twitched, ever so faintly and delicately but unmistakably, and I was able to recognize the picture. . . Why had it taken me so long? It was Demian's face.

Later I often compared the portrait with Demian's true features **as** I remembered them. They were by no means the same even though there was a resemblance 닮은 점. Nonetheless, it was Demian.

Once the early-summer sun slanted oblique and red into a window that faced westward. Dusk was growing in my room. It occurred to me **to** pin the portrait of Beatrice, or Demian, *at* the window crossbar 창틀 and **to** observe the evening sun shine through it. The outlines of the face became blurred 흐려지다 but the red-rimmed eyes, the brightness on the forehead, and the bright red mouth glowed deep and wild from the surface. I sat facing it for a long time, even after the sun had faded, and gradually I began to sense that this was neither Beatrice nor Demian but myself. **Not that** the picture resembled me -- I did not feel that it should -- but it was what determined my life, it was my inner self, my fate or my daemon. That's what my friend would look like if I were to find one ever again. That's what the woman I would love would look like **if** ever I were to

pronounced forehead
두드러진 이마
it=the picture
of its own accord=of itself
저절로

all at once=suddenly
twitch 씰룩거리다
delicately 섬세하게
unmistakably 확실히

take 시간이 걸리다

접속사 **as**: ~한 대로
by no means=never

slant oblique
비스듬히 비쳐들다

to pin ~ to observe
초상화를 ~에 꽂아두고
관찰하고 싶은 생각이 들었다
지각동사+목+목/보(동)
observe ~ shine

red-rimmed 붉게 충혈 된

Not that ~이라는 것은 아니다

determine 결정짓다
Daemon 다이몬:
인간과 신들 중간에
위치하거나, 죽은 영웅의 영혼

가정법 **과거 if**: 만약 ~하게
되면, 내가 ~하게 될 모습이다

love one. That's what my life and death would be like, this was the tone and rhythm of my fate.

During those weeks I had begun to read a book that made a more lasting impression on me than anything I had read before. Even later in life I have rarely experienced a book more intensely, except perhaps Nietzsche. It was a volume of Novalis, containing letters and aphorisms of which I understood only a few but which nevertheless held an inexpressible attraction for me. One of the aphorisms occurred to me now and I wrote it under the picture: "Fate and temperament are two words for one and the same concept." That was clear to me now.

I often caught sight of the girl I called Beatrice but I felt no emotion during these encounters 만남, only a gentle harmony, a presentiment 예감: you and I are linked, but not you, only your picture; you are a part of my fate.

My longing for Max Demian overwhelmed me again. I had had no news of him for years. Once I had met him during a vacation. I realized now that I suppressed this brief encounter in my notes and I realize that it was done out of vanity 허영심 and shame. I have to make up for it.

Thus, during one of my holidays **as** I strolled through my home town, **wearing** the blasé, always slightly weary expression of my bar-crawling days, **peering** into the same old, despised faces of the philistines 속물, I saw my former friend walking toward me. I had **hardly** seen him **when** I flinched. At the same moment I could not help thinking of Franz Kromer. If only Demian had really forgotten that episode! It was so unpleasant to be obligated to him. It was actually a silly children's story

make a lasting impression on ~에게 영원한 인상을 주다

니체: 독일의 철학자
『차라투스트라는 이렇게 말했다』의 저자
노발리스: 니체 이전 독일의 근대철학자
aphorism 격언, 경구, 잠언

Fate and ~ same concept
운명과 기질은 하나의 개념에 붙여진 두 개의 이름이다.

overwhelm 압도하다

suppress A in B:
A를 B에 꼭꼭 숨겨두다

make up for ~를 보충하다

접속사 as=when

blasé 무심한, 무감동한
분사구 2개:
wearing ~한 표정으로
peering ~를 들여다보면서

hardly A when B:
A하자마자 B하다
flinch 꽁무니를 빼다

be obligated to
~에게 빚을 지다

but an obligation 채무 nonetheless. . .

He appeared to wait: would I greet him? When I did so as casually as possible he stretched out his hand. Yes, that was his grip 악력! As firm, warm yet cool, and virile as ever!

He scrutinized my face and said: "You've grown, Sinclair." He himself seemed quite the same, as old or as young as ever.

He joined me and we took a walk, but talked of only inconsequential matters. It occurred to me that I had written him several times without getting a reply. I hoped that he'd forgotten that too, those stupid letters! He did not mention them.

At that time I had not yet met Beatrice and there was no portrait. I was still in the midst of my drunken period. At the outskirts 변두리 of town I asked him to join me for a glass of wine and he did so. At once I made a big show of ordering a whole bottle, filled his glass, clinked mine with his, and displayed my great familiarity with student drinking customs by downing the first glass in one swallow.

"You spend a lot of time in bars, do you?" he asked.

"Well, yes," I replied. "What else is there to do? In the end it's more fun than anything else."

"You think? Maybe so. One part of it is of course very fine -- the intoxication 도취, the bacchanalian element. But I think most people that frequent bars have lost that entirely. It seems to me that going to bars is something genuinely philistine 속물적인. Yes, for one night, with burning torches, a real wild drunk! But again and again, one little glass after the other, I wonder whether that's the real thing or not? Can you see Faust sitting night after night **stooped** over the bar?"

I took a swallow and looked at him with hostility.

"Well, not everybody's Faust," I said curtly 퉁명스럽게.

He looked at me somewhat **taken** aback.

Then he laughed at me in his old lively and superior fashion. "Well, let's not fight over it! In any case, the life of a drunk is presumably livelier than that of the ordinary well-behaved citizen. And then -- I read that once somewhere -- the life of a hedonist is the best preparation for becoming a mystic 신비주의자. People like St. Augustine are always the ones that become visionaries 몽상가. He, too, was first a sensualist and man of the world."

I distrusted him and didn't want him to gain the upper hand under any circumstance. So I said superciliously: "Well, everybody to his own taste. As for me, I've no ambition to become a visionary or anything of the sort."

Demian gave me a brief shrewd look out of half-closed eyes.

"My dear Sinclair," he said slowly, "I didn't intend to tell you anything disagreeable. Besides -- neither of us knows why you happen to be drinking wine at this moment. **That which** is within you and directs your life knows already. It's good to realize that within us there is someone who knows everything, wills 명령하다 everything, does everything better than we ourselves. But excuse me, I must go home."

We exchanged brief good-bys. I stayed on moodily and finished the bottle. When I wanted to leave I discovered that Demian had paid the bill -- **which** put me in an even worse humor.

My thoughts returned to this small incident with Demian. I could not forget him. And the words he said to me in that bar at the edge of town would come to

with hostility 적의에 차서

taken aback 당황하여

that of=the life of

hedonist 쾌락주의자

성 아우구스티누스.
기독교 초기의 교부 (354-430)

sensualist 관능주의자
man of the world
세상물정에 밝은 자. 방탕아

gain the upper hand
~보다 우세하게 되다
superciliously 건방지게

to one's own taste
자신의 취향에 따라 (살다)

shrewd look 날카로운 눈길

that which=what ~한 것

moodily 시무룩하게

which; 데미안이 술값을
지불했다는 사실

would ~하곤 했다

mind, strangely fresh and intact: "It's good to realize that within us there is someone who knows everything."

How I longed for Demian. I had no idea where he was nor how I could reach him. All I knew was that he was presumably studying at some university and that his mother had left town after he completed preparatory school.

I tried to remember whatever I could of Max Demian, reaching back as far as the Kromer episode. How much of what he had said to me over the years returned to mind, was still meaningful today, was appropriate and concerned me! And what he had said on our last and quite disagreeable meeting about a wasted life **leading** to sainthood suddenly also stood clearly before me. Wasn't that exactly what had happened to me? Hadn't I lived in drunkenness and squalor 비참함, **dazed and lost**, until just the opposite had come alive in me with a new zest for life, the longing for purity, the yearning for the sacred?

So I continued to pursue these memories. Night had long since come and now rain was falling. In my memories, too, I heard the rain: it was the hour under the chestnut trees when he had probed me about Franz Kromer and guessed my first secrets. One incident after another came back to me, conversations on the way to school, the Confirmation classes, and last of all my first meeting with him. What had we talked about? I couldn't find it at once, but I gave myself time, **concentrating** intensely. And now even that returned. We had stood before my parents' house after he had told me his version of the story of Cain. Then he had mentioned the old, half-hidden coat of arms **situated** in the keystone above our entrance. He had said that such things interested him and that one ought to attend to them.

intact 본래대로의, 완전한

reaching back
~로 거슬러 올라가

적절하고 나와 관련된
말이었던가!

life leading to
성자에 이른 탕아의 삶

dazed and lost
현혹되어 길을 잃고
zest=taste 풍미, 맛

long since 그 이후 오래

It was ~ when 강조 구문

probe=investigate, ask

concentrating ~
열심히 집중하여
that returned
그 기억도 되살아났다
coat of arms
문장(가문의 상징)
situated in 에 위치한
keystone 아치이맛돌, 종석

- 97 -

That night I dreamed of Demian and the coat of arms.
It kept changing continuously. Demian held it in his
hand, often it was diminutive 작은 and gray, often
powerful and varicolored 가지각색의, but he explained to me
that it was always one and the same thing. In the end
he obliged me to eat the coat of arms! When I had
swallowed it, I felt to my horror that the heraldic bird
was coming to life inside me, had begun to swell up and
devour 삼키다 me from within. **Deathly afraid** I started up
in bed, awoke.

I was wide awake; it was the middle of the night and I
could hear rain pouring into the room. As I got up to
close the window I stepped on something that shone
bright on the floor. In the morning I discovered that it
had been my painting. It lay in a puddle 물웅덩이 and the
paper had warped 뒤틀리다. I placed it between two sheets
of blotting paper inside a heavy book. When I looked at
it again the next day it was dry, but had changed. The
red mouth had faded and contracted 수축하다 a little. It
now looked exactly like Demian's mouth. I set about
painting a fresh picture of the heraldic bird. I could not
remember distinctly what it looked like and certain
details, as I knew, could not be made out even from
close up, because the thing was old and had often been
painted over 덧칠하다. The bird stood or perched on
something, perhaps on a flower or on a basket or a
nest, or on a treetop. I couldn't trouble myself over this
detail and began with what I could visualize clearly. Out
of an indistinct need I at once began to employ loud
colors, **painting** the bird's head a golden yellow.
Whenever the mood took me, I worked on the picture,
bringing it to completion in several days.

Now it represented a bird of prey 육식조 with a proud

coat of arms 문장

diminutive=very small

obliged=forced

heraldic 전령의

swell up 부풀어 오르다

deathly afraid
몹시 두려워하면서
awake-awoke 깨어나다 (동)

awake 깨어난 (형)

지각동사+목+목/보:
hear ~ pouring

blotting paper 압지: 눌러서
물기를 빨아들이는 종이

could not ~ up 가까이 가서
봐도 자세한 것은 알기 어렵다.

perch on
~에 자리 잡고 앉아 있다

visualize 마음에 그리다

indistinct=unclear
loud colors 화려한 색
분사구 2개: 그리고 ~하다
=and painted
=and brought it to
whenever the mood took
me 기분이 내킬 때마다

aquiline sparrow hawk's head, half its body **stuck** in some dark globe out of which it was struggling to free itself as though from a giant egg -- all of this against a sky-blue background. As I continued to scrutinize 조사하다 the sheet 그림 it looked to me more and more like the many-colored coat of arms that had occurred to me in my dream.

aquiline sparrow hawk
매부리 참새 매
분사구 stuck in: ~에 처박은

dark globe 암흑과 같은 지구

I could not have written Demian even if I had known his address. I decided, however -- in the same state of dreamlike presentiment 예감 in which I did everything -- to send him the painting of the sparrow hawk, even if it would never reach him. I added no message, not even my name, carefully trimmed the edges and wrote my friend's former address on it. Then I mailed it.

trim the edges
가장 자리를 정돈하다

I had an exam coming up and had to do more work than usual. The teachers had reinstated me in their favor since I had abruptly changed my previously despicable 비열한 mode of life. **Not that** I had become an outstanding 뛰어난 student, but now neither I nor anyone else gave it any further thought that half a year earlier my expulsion 제적 had seemed almost certain.

reinstate 원상태로 회복시키다

not that ~ 해서가 아니라

My father's letters regained some of their old tone, without reproaches 질책 or threats. Yet I felt no inclination to explain to him or anyone else how the change within me had come about. **It** was an accident **that** this transformation 변화 coincided with my parents' and teachers' wishes. This change did not bring me into the community of the others, did not make me closer to anyone, but actually made me even lonelier. My reformation 개선 seemed to point in the direction of Demian, but even this was a distant fate. I did not know myself, **for** I was too deeply involved. It had begun with Beatrice, but for some time I had been living in **such** an

feel no inclination to
~할 기분은 아니다

가주어 it, 진주어 that

coincide with ~와 일치하다

point in ~의 방향으로 가다

접속사 for: 왜냐하면

such ~ that 구조

unreal world with my paintings and my thoughts of
Demian **that** I'd forgotten all about her, too. I could not
have uttered 말하다 a single word about my dreams and
expectations, my inner change, to anyone, not even if I
had wanted to. But how could I have wanted to?

not even if I ~ to?
내가 말하고 싶어 했더라도
못했을 것이다. 내가 어떻게
그렇게 하기를 바랄 수
있었겠는가?

Chapter V
The Bird Fights Its Way
Out of the egg

Source: https://pixabay.com/ko/

V. "The Bird Fights Its Way Out of the Egg."

My painted dream bird was on its way searching for
my friend. In what seemed the strangest possible manner
a reply reached me.

In my classroom, on my desk, after a break between
two lessons I found a note tucked 찔러 넣어둔 in my book. It
was folded exactly the same as notes classmates of mine
secretly slipped each other during class. I was only
surprised to receive such a note at all, for I had never
had that sort of relationship with any student. I thought
it would turn out to be an invitation to some prank **in**
which I would not participate anyway -- I put the note
unread in the front of my book. I came on it again only
during the lesson.

Playing with the note I unfolded it carelessly and
noticed a few words written on it. One glance was
sufficient. One word stopped me cold; in panic I read on
while cold fear contracted my heart: "The bird flights its
way out of the egg. The egg is the world. Who would be
born must first destroy a world. The bird flies to God.
That God's name is Abraxas."

After reading over these lines a number of times, I
sank into a deep reverie 공상. There could be no doubt
about it, this was Demian's reply. No one else could
know about my painting. He had grasped its meaning
and was helping me interpret 해석하다 it. But how did all of
this fit together? And -- this oppressed me most of all
-- what did Abraxas signify 의미하다? I had never heard
nor read the word. "That God's name is Abraxas."

The lesson went on without my taking in a word of it.
The next began, the last that morning. It was taught by
a young assistant, a Dr. Pollens, who had just completed

in ~ manner 있을 법한 가장
이상한 방법으로

목적격 관/대 생략:
notes (that) classmates ~

at all=at any rate 여하튼

prank 못된 장난

come on it
우연히 그것에 손이 닿다

분사구 play with:
~가지고 놀다가

The bird flights ~ Abraxas
"새는 알을 깨고 나오려고
투쟁한다. 알은 세계이다.
태어나고자 하는 자는 먼저 한
세계를 파괴해야 한다. 그 새는
신에게로 날아간다. 그 신의
이름은 아브락사스이다."
Abraxas 세상을 이원론적으로
보지 않고 선과 악, 두 세계를
모두 인정하는 최고의 신

how ~ together?
어떻게 이 모든 것이 이렇게
잘 연관시켰을까?
oppress 괴롭히다

take in=accept

The next (class) began

his university studies, whom we liked simply because he was young and unpretentious 우쭐대지 않는. Dr. Pollens was guiding us through Herodotus -- one of the few subjects that held any interest for me. But today not even Herodotus could hold my attention. I opened the book mechanically but did not follow the translation and remained sunk deep in my own thoughts. Besides, I had frequently confirmed 확인하다 what Demian had told me once during our Confirmation classes: you can achieve anything you desire passionately enough. If I happened to be involved with my own thoughts during a lesson I did not have to worry that the teacher would call on me. If I was distracted 산만한 or listless, then he would suddenly appear beside me. That had already happened to me. But if I really concentrated, completely **wrapped up** in a thought of my own, then I was protected. I had also experimented with the trick of staring a person down and had found that it worked. **When** still with Demian, I had not succeeded in this; now I often felt that a good deal could be accomplished by a sharp glance, and thought.

I was at present nowhere near Herodotus or school. Suddenly the teacher's voice shot like lightning into my consciousness 의식 and I awoke terrified. I heard his voice, he practically stood next to me, I even thought he had called my name. But he was not looking at me. I relaxed.

Then I heard his voice again. Loudly it pronounced the word "Abraxas." In the course of a long explanation, **whose** beginning I had missed, Dr. Pollens went on: "We ought not consider the opinions of those sects and mystical societies as naive as they appear from the rationalist point of view. Science **as** we know it today

---

Herodotus 헤로도토스
그리스 역사가

remain stuck deep in ~
깊은 생각에 빠져있다.

be involved with ~
나의 생각에 빠져있다.

wrapped up
완전히 ~에 싸여(집중하여)

주어+be동사 생략구조:
When (I was) still with ~
a good deal=lots of things

at present=then 그때는

awake terrified
화들짝 놀라 깨어나다

소유격 관/대 whose:
그것(설명)의 첫 부분
ought not consider
=ought not to consider
those sects: Abraxas를
믿는 영지주의 종파
from the rationalist ~ view
합리주의적 관점에서

was unknown to antiquity 고대. Instead there existed a preoccupation 심취 with philosophical and mystical truths which was highly developed. What grew out of this preoccupation was to some extent merely pedestrian magic and frivolity; perhaps it frequently led to deceptions 속임수 and crimes, but this magic, too, had noble antecedents in a profound philosophy. **As**, for instance, the teachings concerning Abraxas which I cited a moment ago. This name occurs in connection with Greek magical formulas and is frequently considered the name of some magician's helper **such as** certain uncivilized tribes believe in even at present. But it appears that Abraxas has a much deeper significance. We may conceive of the name as **that** of a godhead whose symbolic task is the uniting of godly and devilish elements."

to some extent 어느 정도는
pedestrian 평범한, 저속한
frivolity 부질없는 행위

noble antecedent
칭찬할 만한 선례, 내력
as the teachings
concerning ~에 관한
가르침이 그러하듯

such as ~하는 것과 같은
그런 것으로써
even at present
심지어 현재에도

that of=name of
godhead=god
conceive of ~에 대해
생각하다

The learned little man spoke with intelligence and eagerness but no one paid much attention, and **as** the name Abraxas did not recur, my thoughts turned back to my own affairs.

learned 학식을 갖춘

as 때문에

"Uniting of godly and devilish elements" resounded 울리다 within me. Here was something for my thoughts to cling to. This idea was familiar to me from conversations with Demian. During the last period of our friendship he had said that we had been given a god to worship who represented only one arbitrarily separated half of the world (it was the official, sanctioned 인가된, luminous 빛나는 world), but that we ought to be able to worship the whole world; this meant that we would either have to have a god who was also a devil or institute a cult of the devil alongside the cult of god. And now Abraxas was the god who was both god and devil.

uniting A and B:
A와 B의 결합
cling to 달리다, 고수하다

be given=received 받다

임의로 분리된 절반의 세계
(선의 세계)만을 대표하는 신

institute=begin, initiate
악마의 의식을 시작하다

For a time I pursued this thought eagerly but without

making any headway 진전. I even pored over a whole libraryful of books **seeking** a mention of Abraxas. However, my nature 본성 had never been disposed to this kind of direct and conscious investigation **where** at first one finds only truths that are so much dead weight in one's hand.

The figure of Beatrice **with which** I had occupied myself so intimately 긴밀하게 and fervently 열렬히 gradually became submerged 가라앉다 or, rather, was slowly receding, approaching the horizon more and more, becoming more shadowy 어렴풋한 and remote, paler. She no longer satisfied the longings of my soul.

In the peculiar self-made isolation **in which** I existed like a sleepwalker, a new growth began to take shape within me. The longing for life grew -- or rather the longing for love. My sexual drive, which I had sublimated 승화되다 for a time in the veneration 숭배 of Beatrice, demanded new images and objects. But my desires remained unfulfilled and it was more impossible than ever for me to deceive 속이다 my longings and hope for something from the women **with whom** my comrades tried their luck. I dreamed vividly again, more in fact by day than at night. Images, pictures, desires arose freely within me, drew me away from the outside world **so that** I had a more substantial and livelier relationship with the world of my own creation, with these images and dreams and shadows, than with the actual world around me.

A certain dream, or fantasy, that kept recurring gained in meaning for me. The dream, the most important and enduringly significant of my life, went something like this: I was returning to my father's house -- above the entrance glowed the heraldic bird, yellow on a blue background; in the house itself my mother was coming

pore over 샅샅이 뒤지다

분사구 seeking: 찾아서

be disposed to
~에 대한 마음을 가지고 있다
investigation where ~ hand
처음에는 사람들이 그들이
감당하기에 너무나도 무거운
진실만을 발견하게 되는 조사

The figure ~ with which:
내가 열중했던 ~ 모습

recede 물러나다

remain fulfilled 완성되지
않은 상태로 남아있다
to deceive ~ and hope
갈망을 속이고 나의 친구들이
행복을 찾는 소녀들로부터
무언가를 기대하는 것은

so the 그래서

that keep recurring
계속 반복해서 떠오르는

enduringly significant
지속적으로 중요한
go something like this
대략 이런 식으로 진행되다

toward me -- but as I entered and wanted to embrace her, it was not she but a form I had never set eyes on before, tall and strong, resembling Max Demian and the picture I had painted; yet different, **for** despite its strength it was completely feminine. This form drew me to itself and enveloped 감싸주다 me in a deep, tremulous embrace 떨리는 포옹. I felt a mixture of ecstasy 희열 and horror -- the embrace was at once an act of divine worship and a crime. Too many associations with my mother and friend commingled 뒤섞이다 with this figure **embracing** me. Its embrace violated all sense of reverence, yet it was bliss. Sometimes I awoke from this dream with a feeling of profound 심오한 ecstasy, at others in mortal fear and with a racked conscience as though I had committed some terrible crime.

Only gradually and unconsciously did this very intimate image become linked with the hint about the God I was to search for, the hint that had come to me from the outside. The link grew closer and more intimate and I began to sense that I was calling on Abraxas particularly in this dreamed presentiment. Delight and horror, man and woman commingled 뒤섞이다, the holiest and most shocking were intertwined 뒤얽히다, deep guilt **flashing** through most delicate innocence 우아한 순결: that was the appearance of my love-dream image and Abraxas, too. Love had ceased to be the dark animalistic drive I had experienced at first with fright, nor was it any longer the devout transfiguration 경건한 변모 I had offered to Beatrice. It was both, and yet much more. It was the image of an angel and Satan, man and woman in one flesh, man and beast, the highest good and the worst evil. It seemed that I was destined to live in this fashion, this seemed my preordained fate 미리 정해진 운명. I yearned for it but

접속사 for: 왜냐하면

associations with
~와의 추억들/연상되는 것들

embracing 포옹하는

그것의 포옹은 모든 경외심을 방해했지만 그럼에도 더없는 행복이었다.

in mortal fear
치명적인 두려움에
with a racked conscience
양심의 가책을 느끼며

only 부사 도치구조:
only gradually ~ *did this image become* linked

in ~ presentiment
꿈에서 느낀 예감 속에서

분사구: 그리고 ~하다
=and deep guilt flashed through most ~

목적격 관/대 생략
=drive (that) I had experienced 내가 경험한 충동 with fright 겁에 질려
nor 도치: nor *was it*

be destined to ~할 운명이다

yearn for=long for 갈망하다

feared it at the same time. It was ever-present, **hovering** constantly above me.

The following spring I was to leave the preparatory school and enter a university. I was still undecided, however, as to where and what I was to study. I had grown a thin mustache 콧수염, I was a full-grown man, and yet I was completely helpless and without a goal in life. Only one thing was certain: the voice within me, the dream image. I felt the duty to follow this voice blindly 맹목적으로 wherever it might lead me. But it was difficult and each day I rebelled against it anew. Perhaps I was mad, **as** I thought at moments; perhaps I was not like other men? But I was able to do the same things the others did; with a little effort and industry I could read Plato, was able to solve problems in trigonometry 삼각법 or follow a chemical analysis 화학적 분석. There was only one thing I could not do: wrest the dark secret goal from myself and keep it before me as others did who knew exactly what they wanted to be - professors, lawyers, doctors, artists, however long this would take them and whatever difficulties and advantages this decision would bear in its wake 초기에. This I could not do. Perhaps I would become something similar, but how was I to know? Perhaps I would have to continue my search for years on end and would not become anything, and would not reach a goal. Perhaps I would reach this goal but it would turn out to be an evil, dangerous, horrible one?

I wanted only to try to live in accord with the promptings which came from my true self. Why was that so very difficult?

I made frequent attempts to paint the mighty love apparition 환영 of my dream. I never succeeded. If I **had** I **would have sent** the painting to Demian. Where he was I

hovering ~ 위를 떠돌면서

was to=had to 의무

as to=about=regarding

rebel against ~에 반항하다
접속사 as: ~했듯이
at moments=sometimes

industry=diligence 근면함

wrest A from B:
B로부터 A를 애써 끌어내다
as others who knew ~ 를
아는 사람들이 하는 것처럼

복합 관계부사 + 형용사:
however long ~
얼마나 오래 걸릴지
복합 관계형용사 + 명사:
whatever difficulties ~
어떠한 어려움이 있을 지
in its wake=in the beginning
how was I to know?
=how could I know?
on end=continuously

in accord with ~에 따라서
=according to
prompting 내면의 목소리

가정법 과거완료:
If I had (succeeded)
~했더라면, ~했을 텐데

had no idea. I only knew that we were linked. When would we meet again?

The tranquillity 평온 of the weeks and months of my Beatrice period had long since passed. At that time I felt I had reached a safe harbor, an island of peace. But as always, as soon as I had become accustomed to my condition, as soon as a dream had given me hope, it wilted and became useless. It was futile to sorrow after the loss. I now lived within a fire of unsatisfied longing, of tense expectancy that often drove me completely wild. I often saw the beloved apparition 환영 of my dream with a clarity greater than life, more distinct than my own hand, spoke with it, wept before it, cursed it. I called it mother and knelt down in front of it in tears. I called it my beloved and had a premonition of its ripe 성숙한 all-fulfilling kiss. I called it devil and whore 창녀, vampire and murderer. It enticed 유혹하다 me to the gentlest love-dreams and to devastating shamelessness 지독한 수치심, nothing was too good and precious, nothing was too wicked and low for it.

I experienced the whole of that winter as one unending inner turbulence, which I find difficult to describe. I had long since become used to my loneliness - that did not oppress me: I lived with Demian, the sparrow hawk 새매, with the mighty apparition of my dream that was both my fate and my beloved. This was enough to sustain me, for everything pointed toward vastness and space - it all pointed toward Abraxas. But none of these dreams, none of these thoughts obeyed me, none were at my beck and call, I could color none of them as I pleased. They came and took me, I was ruled by them, was their vessel.

However, I was well armed against the outside world. I was no longer afraid of people; even my fellow students

wilt=wither 시들다
futile=useless, in vain 헛된
sorrow 슬픔에 잠기다

tense expectancy
긴장된 기대

have a premonition of
~를 예감하다

for it 그것에 비하면

turbulence (감정의) 동요

that=my loneliness

sustain 지탱하다

접속사 for: 왜냐하면
toward vastness and space
광대함과 우주를 향하다

be at one's beck and call
내 마음대로 부리다
접속사 as: 내가 원하는 대로

vessel=ship, boat, bowl

be well armed against
~에 대해 잘 무장되어 있다

had come to know this and treated me with a secret
respect that often brought a smile to my lips. If I wanted
to I could see through most of them and startled them
occasionally. Only I rarely or never tried. I was always
preoccupied with myself. And I longed desperately 몹시 to
really live for once, to give something of myself to the
world, to enter into a relationship and battle with it.
Sometimes when I ran through the streets in the
evening, **unable** to return before midnight because I was
so restless 불안한, I felt that now at this very moment I
would have to meet my beloved -- as she walked past
me at the next street corner, called to me from the
nearest window. At other times all of this seemed
unbearably painful and I was prepared to commit
suicide.

Just then I found a strange refuge 피난처-- "by chance,"
as they say -- though I believe there is no such thing.
If you need something desperately and find it, this is not
an accident; your own craving and compulsion leads you
to it.

Twice or three times during my walks I had heard
organ music coming from a small church at the edge of
town. I had not stopped to listen. The next time I passed
this church I heard the music again and recognized
Bach. I went to the door, found it locked, and because
the street was almost deserted I sat down on a
curbstone next to the church, turned up my coat collar,
and listened. It was not a big organ but it had good
tone. It was being played with a strange, highly personal
expression of purpose and tenacity 고집 that gave the
impression of prayer. I felt that the organist knew the
treasures hidden in the music, that he was wooing,
hammering at the gate, wrestling for this treasure **as** for

see through 간파하다

be preoccupied with
~에 몰두하다

live for (the world) once
다시 한 번 세상을 살아보다

(being) unable to return
돌아 올 수 없어서

접속사 **as**=when

(and as she) called to me
그녀가 나에게 소리치다

be prepared to
~할 준비가 되어 있다
commit suicide 자살하다

by chance=accidently 우연히

접속사 **as**: ~하듯이
such thing 그런 우연

craving 갈망
compulsion
억누르기 힘든 욕망

hear ~ coming from

find 5형식=find+목+목/보
find ~ locked
deserted 사람의 왕래가 없는

curbstone (보도의) 연석

woo 호소하다
hammer 망치로 두드리다
as for 마치 자신의 목숨을
위해 싸우듯

- 109 -

his life. My knowledge of music is technically very limited but from childhood on I have had an intuitive grasp, have sensed music as something self-evident 자명한 within me. The organist also played something more modern - it could have been Max Reger. The church was almost completely dark, only a very thin beam of light penetrated the window closest to me. I waited until the music ceased and then paced back and forth until I saw the organist leave the church. He was still young, though older than I, square-shouldered and squat, and he moved off rapidly with vigorous yet seemingly reluctant strides 걸음걸이.

From then on I occasionally sat outside the church or paced up and down before it during the evening hours. Once I even found the door open and sat for half an hour in a pew, **shivering** against the cold, yet happy as long as the organist played in the loft. I not only distinguished 알아내다 his personality in the music he played -- every piece he performed also had affinity with the next, a secret connection. Everything he played was full of faith, surrender 굴복, and devotion 헌신. Yet not devout after the fashion of churchgoers and pastors, devout the way pilgrims 순례자 and mendicants 탁발수사 were in the Middle Ages, devout with that unconditional surrender 굴복 to a universal feeling that transcends all confessions. He also played music composed prior to Bach, and the old Italians. And all this music said the same thing, all of it expressed **what** was in the musician's soul: longing, a most intimate atonement with the world and a violent wrenching loose, a burning hearkening to one's own dark soul, an intoxicating surrender 도취적인 굴복 and deep curiosity about the miraculous 경이로운 것들.

intuitive grasp
직관적인 이해력

막스 레거: 독일의 낭만주의 작곡가. 바로크 형식으로 된 오르간 곡으로 유명

penetrate the window
창문을 통해 흘러나오다
cease=stop

see ~ leave

square-shoulder and squat
체구가 다부지고 땅딸막한

it=the church

pew 신도들이 앉는 의자
shivering against the cold
추위로 떨면서
loft 교회의 위층

have affinity with
~와 연관이 있다

devout after the fashion of
~를 닮아 경건한

transcend all confessions
모든 고백을 초월하다
composed prior to
~ 이전에 작곡된

관/대 what: ~한 것

intimate atonement with ~
세상에 대한 마음속에서 우러난 속죄
a violent wrenching (which was) loose 속박 받지 않는 격하게 비틀거리는 해방감
a burning hearkening to
~에 대한 열렬한 경청

- 110 -

Once when I shadowed 미행하다 the organist after he left the church, I saw him enter a small tavern 술집 on the edge of town. I could not resist following him in. For the first time I could see him clearly. He sat at a table in the far corner of the small room. He wore a black felt hat. A jug 술병 of wine stood before him. His face looked **as** I suspected 짐작하다 it would. He was ugly and a little wild, inquisitive and pigheaded 고집이 센, capricious and determined, yet his mouth had a soft childlike quality. All his masculinity 남성다움 and strength were concentrated in eyes and forehead, while the lower part of the face was sensitive and immature, uncontrolled and somehow very soft. The irresolute, boyish chin appeared to contradict the forehead and eyes - which I liked, those dark-brown eyes, full of pride and hostility 적의.

I sat down opposite him without saying a word. We were the only two guests in the tavern. He gave me a look as though he wanted to shoo me away. But I did not budge 움직이다, and stared back unmoved until he grumbled morosely: "What on earth are you staring at? Is there something you want?"

"No, I don't want anything from you," I said. "You've given me a great deal already."

He knitted his brows.

"So, you're a music lover. I find it nauseating to be crazy about music."

I did not let him intimidate 겁주다 me.

"I have listened to you often, back there in the church," I said. "But I don't want to trouble you. I thought I might find something, something special; I really don't know what. But don't pay any attention to me. I can listen to you in church."

"But I always lock it."

see ~ enter

resist ~ing ~를 저항하다

felt 펠트: 모직이나 털을 압축해서 만든 부드럽고 두꺼운 천

as ~ 그럴 것이라고 내가 짐작한 대로
inquisitive 캐묻기를 좋아하는
capricious 변덕이 심한
resolute=determined 단호한

irresolute 우유부단한
appear to contradict ~와 대조되어 보이다

shoo ~ away 쉬 하며 내쫓다

grumble morosely 언짢게 중얼거리다

knit one's brows 눈살을 찌푸리다
nauseating 구역질나는

let ~ intimate

"Not very long ago you forgot and I sat inside. Usually I stand outside or sit on the curb."

"Really? Next time you can come inside, it's warmer. All you have to do is knock at the door. But you have to bang hard and not while I'm playing. Go ahead now – what did you want to tell me? You're quite young yet, probably a student of some sort. Are you a musician?"

"No. I like listening to music, but only the kind you play, completely unreserved music, the kind that makes you feel that a man is shaking heaven and hell. I believe I love that kind of music because it is amoral 선악을 초월한. Everything else is **so** moral **that** I'm looking for something that isn't. Morality has always seemed to me insufferable. I can't express it very well. — Do you know that there must be a god who is both god and devil at one and the same time? There is supposed to have been one once. I heard about it."

The musician pushed his wide hat back a little and shook the hair out of his eyes, all the while peering at me. He lowered his face across the table.

Softly and expectantly 기대하며 he asked: "What's the name of the god you mentioned?"

"Unfortunately I know next to nothing about him, actually only his name. He is called Abraxas."

The musician blinked suspiciously around him **as though** someone might be eavesdropping. Then he moved closer to me and said in a whisper: "That's what I thought. Who are you?"

"A student at the prep school."

"How did you happen to hear about Abraxas?"

"By accident."

He struck the table **so that** wine spilled out of his glass. "By accident! Don't talk shit, young fellow! One

unreserved 숨김없는
make ~ feel

so ~ that 구조

morality 선악, 도덕

one=such a god
이전에 그런 신이 있었다는
이야기를 들었다.

all the while ~ 동안 내내

know next to nothing about
~에 대해서 아는 것이 거의 없다.

누가 엿듣기라도 하는 듯
의심스러운 눈초리로 사방을
둘러보다. eavesdrop 엿듣다

so that 접속사: 그래서
Don't talk shit.
허튼소리 하지 마.

doesn't hear about Abraxas by accident, and don't you forget it. I will tell you more about him. I know a little."

He fell silent and moved his chair back. When I looked at him full of expectation, he made a face.

"Not here. Some other time. There, take these."

He reached in his coat, which he had not taken off, and drew out a few roasted chestnuts and threw them to me.

I said nothing, took them, ate and felt content.

content=satisfied

"All right," he whispered after a moment. "Where did you find out about — Him?"

I did not hesitate to tell him.

"I was alone and desperate 자포자기한 at one time," I began. "Then I remembered a friend I had had several years back **who** I felt knew much more than I did. I had painted something, a bird struggling out of the globe. I sent him this painting. After a time I found a piece of paper with the following words written on it: "The bird fights its way out of the egg. The egg is the world. Who would be born must first destroy a world. The bird flies to God. That God's name is Abraxas.""

주격 관/대+삽입구+동사:
a friend who *I felt* knew ~

He made no reply. We shelled our chestnuts and drank our wine.

shell 껍질을 벗기다

"Another glass?" he asked.

"No, thanks. I don't like drinking."

He laughed, a little disappointed.

"As you like. It's different with me. I'll stay but you can run along if you want."

It's different with me.
=I like drinking.

When I joined him the next time, after he had played the organ, he was not very communicative 수다스러운. He led me down an alley and through an old and impressive house and up to a large, somewhat dark and neglected room. Except for a piano, nothing in it gave a hint of

neglected 방치된, 황폐한

- 113 -

his being a musician — but a large bookcase and a desk gave the room an almost scholarly air.

"How many books you have!" I exclaimed.

"Part of them are from my father's library — **in whose house** I live. Yes, young man, I'm living with my parents but I can't introduce you to them. My acquaintances 지인 aren't regarded very favorably in this house. I'm the black sheep. My father is fabulously respectable and an important pastor and preacher in this town. And I, so that you know the score at once, am his talented and promising son who has gone astray and, to some extent, even mad. I was a theology student 신학도 but shortly before my state exams I left this very respectable department; that is, not entirely, not in so far as it concerns my private studies, for I'm still most interested to see what kinds of gods people have devised 생각해내다 for themselves. Otherwise, I'm a musician at present and it looks as though I will receive a small post 자리 as an organist somewhere. Then I'll be back in the employ of the church again."

As much as the feeble light from the small table lamp permitted, I glanced along the spines of the books and noticed Greek, Latin, and Hebrew titles. Meanwhile my acquaintance had lain down on the floor and was busying himself with something.

"Come," he called after a moment, "we want to practice a bit of philosophy. That means: keep your mouth shut, lie on your stomach, and meditate 명상하다."

He struck a match and lit paper and wood in the fireplace in front of which he sprawled 기어가다. The flames leapt high, he stirred and fed them with the greatest care. I lay down beside him on the worn-out 낡은 carpet. For about an hour we lay on our stomachs silent

전치사+소유격 관/대
=and I live in his house.

fabulously respectable
굉장히 존경받는

score 현재의 상황, 진상
promising 전도유망한
go astray 잘못된 길을 가다

state exams
국가에서 주관하는 시험
respectable department
존경받는 학과(부)/학업
not in so far as it
concerns my private studies
내 개인적인 연구에 관한 한,
신학을 중단한 것은 아니다.

otherwise 그 외에

the spines of the books
책꽂이에 나란히 진열된 책

매우 조심스럽게 불을 휘젓고
장작을 더 넣었다

before the shimmering wood, **watching** the flames shoot up and roar, sink down and double over, flicker and twitch, and in the end brood quietly on sunken embers.

"Fire worship was by no means the most foolish thing ever invented," he murmured to himself at one point.

Otherwise neither of us said a word. I stared fixedly into the flames, lost myself in dreams and stillness, recognized figures in the smoke and pictures in the ashes. Once I was startled. My companion threw a piece of resin 송진 into the embers 불씨: a slim flame shot up and I recognized the bird with the yellow sparrow hawk's head. In the dying embers, red and gold threads 실 ran together into nets, letters of the alphabet appeared, memories of faces, animals, plants, worms, and snakes. As I emerged from my reveries 몽상 I looked at my companion, his chin **resting** on his fists, **staring** fanatically into the ashes with complete surrender.

"I have to go now," I said softly.

"Go ahead then. Good-by."

He did not get up. The lamp had gone out: I groped my way through the dark rooms and hallways of the bewitched old house. Once outside, I stopped and looked up along its façade. Every window was dark. A small brass plate on the front door gleamed 번쩍이다 in the light from a street lamp. On it I read the words: "Pistorius, pastor primarius." **Not until** I was at home and sat in my little room after supper **did it occur** to me that I had not heard anything about either Abraxas or Pistorius — we'd exchanged hardly a dozen words. But I was very satisfied with my visit. And for our next meeting he had promised to play an exquisite piece of old music, an organ passacaglia by Buxtehude. Without my being entirely aware of it, the organist Pistorius had given me my first

shimmering wood
아른거리며 타는 나무
watching A shoot up ~
불길이 치솟고 굉음을 내고,
가라앉고 겹쳐지며, 깜빡거리며
움직이다가 마침내 가라앉은
불씨 위로 조용히 내려앉는
것을 보면서
(주격 관/대+be동사) 생략
=thing (that was) ever
invented ~
fire worship 배화/불 숭배

slim flame 가느다란 불길

his chin resting, staring
주먹위에 턱을 괴고, ~을 미친
듯 응시하고 있는

grope=search

bewitched 마법에 걸린

facade=the front of the
building 정면, 외관
brass plate 황동 판

수석 목사 피스토리우스

부정어 도치구조:
not until 주어+동사(A)
조동사+주어+동사(B):
A하고서야 비로소 B하다

exquisite piece 정교한 곡
passacaglia 파사칼리아,
3박자의 완만한 춤곡
북스테후데: 덴마크의 오르간
연주자, 작곡가

lesson when we were sprawled on the floor before the fire in his depressing hermit's room. Staring into the blaze had been a tonic 강장제 for me, **confirming** tendencies that I had always had but never cultivated 갈고 닦다. Gradually some of them were becoming comprehensible to me.

Even as a young boy I had been in the habit of gazing at bizarre natural phenomena, not so much **observing** them as surrendering to their magic, their confused, deep language. Long gnarled 꼬인 tree roots, colored veins in rocks, patches of oil floating on water, light-refracting flaws in glass — all these things had held great magic for me at one time: water and fire particularly, smoke, clouds, and dust, but most of all the swirling specks of color that swam before my eyes **the minute** I closed them. I began to remember all this in the days after my visit to Pistorius, for I noticed that a certain strength and joy, an intensification 강화 of my self-awareness that I had felt since that evening, I owed exclusively to this prolonged staring into the fire. It was remarkably comforting and rewarding.

To the few experiences which helped me along the way toward my life's true goal I added this new one: the observation 관찰 of such configurations 형태. The surrender to Nature's irrational, strangely confused formations produces in us a feeling of inner harmony with the force responsible for these phenomena. We soon fall prey to the temptation of thinking of them as being our own moods, our own creations, and see the boundaries separating us from Nature begin to quiver and dissolve. We become acquainted with that state of mind **in which** we are unable to decide whether the images on our retina 망막 are the result of impressions coming from without or from within. Nowhere as in this exercise can we discover so easily and simply to what extent we are creative, to what extent our soul partakes of the constant creation of the world. For **it is** the same indivisible divinity 불가분의 신성 **that** is active through us and in Nature, and if the outside world **were to** be destroyed, a single one of us **would be** capable of rebuilding it: mountain and stream, tree and leaf, root and flower, yes, every natural form is latent within us, originates in the soul **whose** essence is eternity 불멸, **whose** essence we cannot know but **which** most often intimates itself to us **as** the power to love and create.

Not until many years later did I find these observations of mine confirmed 확인된, in a book by Leonardo da Vinci, who describes at one point how good, how intensely interesting it is to look at a wall many people have spit on. Confronted with each stain 침 얼룩 on the wet wall, he must have felt the same as Pistorius and I felt before the fire.

The next time we were together, the organist gave me an explanation: "We always define the limits of our personality 개인의 한계 too narrowly. In general, we **count** as part of our personality only that which we can recognize **as** being an individual trait 개인의 특성 or **as** diverging from the norm. But we consist of everything the world consists of, each of us, and just **as** our body contains the genealogical table of evolution 진화의 계보 as far back as the fish and even much further, so we bear everything in our soul **that** once was alive in the soul of men. Every god and devil that ever existed, be it among the Greeks, Chinese, or Zulus, are within us, exist as latent possibilities, as wishes, as alternatives 대안. If the human race **were to** vanish from the face of the earth

save for one halfway talented child that had received no
education, this child **would rediscover** the entire course
of evolution, it **would be** capable of producing everything
once more, gods and demons, paradises, commandments,
the Old and New Testament 구약과 신약."

"Yes, fine," I replied. "But what is the value of the
individual in that case? Why do we continue striving if
everything has been completed within us?"

"Stop!" exclaimed Pistorius. "There's an immense
difference between simply carrying the world within us
and being aware of it. A madman can spout ideas that
remind you of Plato, and a pious little seminary student
rethinks deep mythological correspondences 신화적 대응물
found among the Gnostics or in Zoroaster. But he isn't
aware of them. He is a tree or stone, at best 기껏해야 an
animal, as long as he is not conscious. But as soon as
the first spark of recognition dawns within him he is a
human being. You wouldn't consider all the bipeds you
pass on the street human beings simply because they
walk upright and carry their young in their bellies nine
months! It is obvious how many of them are fish or
sheep, worms or angels, how many are ants, how many
are bees! Well, each one of them contains the possibility
of becoming human, but only by having an intimation of
these possibilities, partially even by learning to make
himself conscious of them; only in this respect 이 점에 있어서
are these possibilities his."

This was the general drift 흐름 of our conversations.
They rarely confronted me with anything completely new,
anything altogether astonishing. But everything, even the
most ordinary matters, resembled gentle persistent
hammer blows on the same spot within me; all of them
helped me to form myself, all of them helped to peel off

save for=except for

it=the child

commandments 율법

spout ideas=come up with
ideas 아이디어를 내 놓다
pious seminary student
경건한 신학도

Gnostics 그노시스파, 영지주의:
종교적 정통과 권위에 대항하여
개인적 영적 지식을 강조
Xoroaster 조로아스터파:
차라투스트라가 창시한
페르시아의 종교. 불을 숭배,
선과 악의 이원론을 가르침
dawn 나타나기 시작하다
bipeds 두발달린 것들
consider all ~ (as) human
beings A를 B로 간주하다

have an intimation of
~에 대해 예감하다

부사구 다음 도치구조:
are these possibilities his

they=our conversations
confront A with B:
A를 B와 직면하게 하다
rarely 거의 ~아니다
resemble ~ 부드럽고
지속적인 망치질을 닮다(하다)

peel off 피부의 층을 벗겨내다

layers of skin, to break eggshells, and after each blow I lifted my head a little higher, a little more freely, until my yellow bird pushed its beautiful raptor's head out of the shattered shell of the terrestrial globe.

Frequently we also told each other our dreams. Pistorius knew how to interpret 해석하다 them. An example of this comes to mind just now. I dreamed I was able to fly, but in such a way that I seemed catapulted into the air and lost all control. The feeling of flying exhilarated 유쾌하게 하다 me, but exhilaration 유쾌함 turned to fear when I saw myself driven higher and higher, becoming more and more powerless. At that instant I made the saving discovery **that** I could regulate 조절하다 the rise or fall of my flight by holding or releasing my breath.

Pistorius' comment was: "The impetus 추진력 that makes you fly is our great human possession 재산. Everybody has it. It is the feeling of being linked with the roots of power, but one soon becomes afraid of this feeling. It's damned dangerous! That is why most people shed their wings and prefer to walk and obey the law. But not you. You go on flying. And look! You discover that you gradually begin to master your flight, that to the great general force that tears you upward there is added a delicate, small force of your own, an organ, a steering mechanism 조종 장치. How marvelous! Lacking that, you would be drawn up to the heights, powerless — which is what happens to madmen. **They** possess 가지다 deeper intimations 예감 than people who remain earth-bound, but they have no key and no steering mechanism and roar off into infinity. But you, Sinclair, you are going about it the right way. How? You probably don't know yourself. You are doing it with a new organ 기관, with something that regulates your breathing. And now you will realize

until ~ globe
나의 황금 새가 깨어진 세계의 껍질에서 맹금의 머리를 내밀고 나올 때까지

seem/be catapulted into
~로 발사되다, ~로 치솟다

make the saving discovery
구원의 발견을 하다=안심하다
(so) that 그래서 ~하다

hold or release breath
호흡을 참거나 내뱉다

dammed 터무니없이, 심하게
shed (허물/날개)를 벗다

that 이하를 발견하다

tear ~ upward ~를 낚아채어 위로 들어 올리다
to the great general force
거대하고 보편적 힘에
부사구 다음 도치구조:
to the general ~ is added *a delicate, small force* ~
A is added to B: *A*가 B에 더해지다
be drawn up to the heights
공중에 계속 떠 있다
earth-bound 날지 못하는
They=madmen
roar off into infinity
포효하며 심연/영원 속으로 사라지다.

how little 'individuality' your soul has in its deepest reaches. For **it** does not invent this regulator 조절 장치! **It** is not new! You've borrowed it: it has existed for thousands of years. It is the organ with which fish regulate their equilibrium 평형 – the air bladder 부레. And in fact among the fish there are still a few strange primeval genera 원시적인 종 where the air bladder functions as a kind of lung 폐 and can be used on occasion as a breathing mechanism 호흡장치. In other words, exactly like the lung which you in your dream use as a flying bladder."

He even brought out a zoology 동물학 book and showed me the names and illustrations 삽화 of these anachronistic fish 진화가 덜 된 물고기. And with a peculiar shudder 전율 I felt that an organ from an earlier period of evolution was still alive within me.

individuality 개성
in its deepest reaches (영혼의) 가장 깊은 곳에서
it=your soul
it=regulator

genus의 복수=genera 종

on occasion=sometimes

flying bladder 비행할 때 사용하는 바람 주머니

Chapter VI
Jacob Wrestling

http://www.daheshmuseum.org/collection/zoom.php?object=bonnatl_1

VI. Jacob Wrestling

It is impossible to recount briefly all that Pistorius the eccentric 괴상한 musician told me about Abraxas. Most important was that what I learned from him represented a further step on the road toward myself. At that time, I was an unusual young man of eighteen, precocious 조숙한 in a hundred ways, in a hundred others immature and helpless. When I compared myself with other boys my age I often felt proud and conceited 우쭐한 but just as often humiliated 창피한 and depressed 우울한. Frequently I considered myself a genius, and just as frequently, crazy. I did not succeed in participating in the life of boys my age, was often consumed by self-reproach 자책 and worries: I was helplessly separated from them, I was debarred from life.

Pistorius, who was himself a full-grown eccentric 괴짜, taught me to maintain my courage and self-respect. By always finding something of value in what I said, in my dreams, my fantasies and thoughts, by never making light of them, always giving them serious consideration, he became my model.

"You told me," he said, "that you love music because it is amoral. That's all right with me. But in that case you can't allow yourself to be a moralist either. You can't compare yourself with others: if Nature has made you a bat, you shouldn't try to be an ostrich 타조. You consider yourself odd at times, you accuse yourself of taking a road different from most people. You have to unlearn that. Gaze into the fire, into the clouds, and as soon as the inner voices begin to speak, surrender to them, don't ask first whether it's permitted or would please your teachers or father, or some god. You will ruin

야곱: 이삭의 둘째 아들. 이스라엘 백성의 조상으로 불림. 장자의 권리를 얻어내기 위해 쌍둥이 형 에사오를 속이고 메소포타미아의 하란으로 도망.

recount briefly
짧게 이야기하다

in a hundred ways
수백 가지의 면/방식에서
others=other ways
others (I was) immature ~
but just as 그러나 그만큼

be consumed by
~에 사로잡히다
be debarred from
~에서 쫓겨나다/제외되다

make light of 가볍게 여기다

amoral 도덕을 초월한

unlearn=forget

yourself if you do that. That way you will become earthbound, a vegetable. Sinclair, our god's name is Abraxas and he is God and Satan and he contains both the luminous and the dark world. Abraxas does not take exception to any of your thoughts, any of your dreams. Never forget that. But he will leave you once you've become blameless and normal. Then he will leave you and look for a different vessel 그릇 in which to brew his thoughts."

세속적인 것에 묶여 식물과 같은 인간이 되다

take exception to
~에 이의를 제기하다

blameless 나무랄 데 없는
그의 생각을 양조할 다른 용기/그릇

Among all my dreams the dark dream of love was the most faithful. How often I dreamed that I stepped beneath the heraldic bird into our house, wanted to draw my mother to me and instead held the great, half-male, half-maternal woman in my arms, of whom I was afraid but who also attracted me violently. And I could never confess this dream to my friend. I kept it to myself even after I had told him everything else. It was my corner, my secret, my refuge.

heraldic bird into ~
우리 집 대문 위에 부착된 가문의 문장을 나타내는 새

corner 모퉁이, 비밀장소

When I felt bad I asked Pistorius to play Buxtehude's passacaglia. Then I would sit in the dusk-filled church completely involved in this unusually intimate, self-absorbed music, music **that** seemed to listen to itself, **that** comforted 위로하다 me each time, prepared me more and more to heed my own inner voices.

북스테후데의 파사칼리아

dusk-filled 어스름 가득한

be involved in ~에 몰두하다
in this intimate ~ music
유별나게 친밀하고 자기도취적인 음악
music that ~하는 음악

heed=pay attention to

At times we stayed even after the music had ceased: we watched the weak light filter through the high, sharply arched windows and lose itself in the church.

지각동사+목+목/보(동):
watch ~ filter through
약한 빛이 ~를 통해 여과되어 사라지는 것을 보다

"It sounds odd," said Pistorius, "that I was a theology student once and almost became a pastor. But I only committed a mistake of form. My task and goal still is to be a priest. Yet I was satisfied too soon and offered myself to Jehovah before I knew about Abraxas. Oh, yes, each and every religion is beautiful; religion is soul, no

commit a mistake of form
형식상의 과오를 범하다

offer A to B:
A를 B에 바치다
Jehovah 여호와, 하나님

matter whether you take part in Christian communion or make a pilgrimage to Mecca."

"But in that case," I intervened 끼어들다, "you actually could have become a pastor."

"No, Sinclair. I **would have had** to lie. Our religion is practiced as though it were something else, something totally ineffectual. If worst came to worst I might become a Catholic, but a Protestant pastor — no! The few genuine 진짜 believers — I do know a few - prefer the literal interpretation. I would not be able to tell them, for example, that Christ is not a person for me but a hero, a myth, an extraordinary shadow image **in which** humanity has painted itself on the wall of eternity. And the others, that come to church to hear a few clever phrases, to fulfill an obligation 의무, not to miss anything, and so forth, what should I have said to them? Convert them? Is that what you mean? But I have no desire to. A priest does not want to convert, he merely wants to live among believers, among his own kind. He wants to be the instrument and expression for the feeling **from which** we create our gods."

He interrupted 중단하다 himself. Then continued: "My friend, our new religion, **for which** we have chosen the name Abraxas, is beautiful. It is the best we have. But it is still a fledgling 풋내기. Its wings haven't grown yet. A lonely religion isn't right either. There has to be a community 공동체, there must be a cult 의식 and intoxicants, feasts and mysteries. . ."

He sank into a reverie and became lost within himself.

"Can't one perform mysteries all by oneself or among a very small group?" I asked hesitantly.

"Yes, one can." He nodded. "I've been performing them for a long time by myself. I have cults of my own for

기독교 단체, 교회
make a pilgrimage to Mecca 메카로 순례하다
메카: 이슬람교의 교조인 마호메트의 탄생지, 이슬람교 최고의 성지.

(If I had become a pastor) I would have had to lie.

ineffectual 효과가 없는
if worst came to worst 최악의 상황이 닥친다면

literal interpretation 문자/글자 그대로의 해석

image in which ~ eternity 인류가 영원의 벽에 그린 특별한 상상적 이미지

convert 개종하다

for which 우리의 새로운 종교를 위해

intoxicants 종교에 심취한 자

reverie 몽상, 환상

perform mysteries (이교의) 신비 의식을 행하다

which I would be sentenced to years in prison if anyone should ever find out about them. Still, I know that it's not the right thing either."

If ~ should 가정법: 가능성, 확률이 희박할 때 사용

Suddenly he slapped me on the shoulder so that I started up. "Boy," he said intensely 진지하게, "you, too, have mysteries of your own. I know that you must have dreams that you don't tell me. I don't want to know them. But I can tell you: live those dreams, play with them, build altars 제단 to them. It is not yet the ideal but it points in the right direction. Whether you and I and a few others will renew the world someday remains to be seen. But within ourselves we must renew it each day, otherwise we just aren't serious 진심의. Don't forget that! You are eighteen years old, Sinclair, you don't go running to prostitutes 매춘부. You must have dreams of love, you must have desires. Perhaps you're made in such a way that you are afraid of them. Don't be. They are the best things you have. You can believe me. I lost a great deal when I was your age by violating those dreams of love. One shouldn't do that. When you know something about Abraxas, you cannot do this any longer. You aren't allowed to be afraid of anything, you can't consider prohibited anything that the soul desires."

start up (with surprise) 놀라서 움찔하다

must have dreams 꿈을 가지고 있음에 틀림없다

remain to be seen ~인지 아닌지는 두고 볼 일이다

must=should

you are made in ~ way 너는 ~한 방식으로 만들어지다

violate 어기다, 위반하다

(목적보어) 도치구조: consider (anything that the soul desires) prohibited

Startled, I countered: "But you can't do everything that comes to your mind! You can't kill someone because you detest 혐오하다 him."

(being) startled: 깜짝 놀라서
counter 되받아치다

He moved closer to me.

"Under certain circumstances, even that. Yet it is a mistake most of the time. I don't mean that you should simply do everything that pops into your head. No. But you shouldn't harm and drive away those ideas that make good sense by exorcising them or moralizing about them. Instead of crucifying yourself or someone else you

even that 그렇게 할 수도 있다

make good sense 훌륭한 가치를 만들어 내다
by exorcising or moralizing 주문/마법을 사용하여 몰아내거나 도덕화 함으로써

can drink wine from a chalice and contemplate the mystery of the sacrifice. Even without such procedures you can treat your drives and so-called temptations with respect and love. Then they will reveal their meaning — and they all do have meaning. If you happen to think of something truly mad or sinful again, if you want to kill someone or want to commit some enormity 극악, Sinclair, think at that moment that it is Abraxas fantasizing within you! The person whom you would like to do away with is of course never Mr. X but merely a disguise 위장. If you hate a person, you hate something in him that is part of yourself. What isn't part of ourselves doesn't disturb us."

Never before *had Pistorius said* anything to me that had touched me as deeply as this. I could not reply. But what had affected me most and in the strangest way was the similarity of this exhortation 충고 to Demian's words, which I had been carrying around with me for years. They did not know each other, yet both of them had told me the same tiling.

"The things we see," Pistorius said softly, "are the same things that are within us. There is no reality except the one contained within us. That is why so many people live such an unreal life. They take the images outside them for reality and never allow the world within to assert itself. You can be happy that way. But once you know the other interpretation 해석, you no longer have the choice of following the crowd. Sinclair, the majority's path is an easy one, ours is difficult."

A few days later, after I had twice waited in vain, I met him late at night as he came seemingly blown around a corner by the cold night wind, stumbling all over himself, dead drunk. I felt no wish to call him. He went past me without seeing me, staring in front of

crucify 십자가에 못 박다
chalice 성배(잔)
contemplate ~를 계획하다

do have=have의 강조 용법

fantasize 상상/공상하다

do away with 제거하다

Mr. X 실존인물
nerver A but merely B:
절대 A가 아니라 B일 뿐이다

disturb us
우리의 마음을 어지럽히다

부정부사 도치구조:
never before *had Pistorius said*

피스토리우스의 권고/충고가
데미안의 말과 유사하다

우리가 겪는 모든 현실은 우리
안에 내재되어 있다
the one (which is)
contained within us

assert oneself
제 주장을 내세우다

came seemingly blown by
찬 밤바람에 의해 불려온 듯
왔다

himself with bewildered eyes **shining**, as though he followed something darkly calling out of the unknown. I followed him the length of one street; he drifted along as though pulled by an invisible string, with a fanatic gait, yet loose, like a ghost. Sadly I returned home to my unfulfilled dreams.

So that is how he renews the world within himself! it occurred to me. At the same moment I felt that was a low, moralizing thought. What did I know of his dreams? Perhaps he walked a more certain path in his intoxication than I within my dream.

I had noticed a few times during the breaks between classes that a fellow student I had never paid any previous attention to seemed to seek me out. He was a delicate 가냘픈, weak-looking boy with thin red-blond hair, and the look in his eyes and his behavior seemed unusual. One evening when I was coming home he was lying in wait for me in the alley 샛길. He let me walk past, then followed me and stopped when I did before the front door.

"Is there something you want from me?" I asked him.

"I would only like to talk with you once," he said shyly. "Be so kind as to walk with me for a moment."

I followed him, sensing that he was excited and full of expectation. His hands trembled.

"Are you a spiritualist?" 심령술사 he asked suddenly.

"No, Knauer," I said laughing. "Not in the least What makes you think I am?"

"But then you must be a theosophist?" 접신술사

"Neither."

"Oh, don't be so reticent! I can feel there's something special about you. There's a look in your eyes. . . I'm positive you communicate with spirits. I'm not asking out

---

with ~ shining:
당황한 눈을 반짝이며
something (which was) darkly calling out of ~
미지의 세계에서 은밀하게 부르는 어떤 것
(주어+be) 생략구조:
as though (he was) pulled-
fanatic gait 광적인 걸음걸이

a low, moralizing thought
저열한, 도덕적 사고

in his intoxication
만취한 상태에서

a student (that) I had never paid attention to

사역동사 let ~ walk past

Knauer 크나우어

reticent 과묵한, 삼가 하는
Don't be so reticent!
그렇게 숨기지 마!

of idle curiosity, Sinclair. No, I am a seeker myself, you know, and I'm so very alone."

"Go ahead, tell me about it," I encouraged him. "I don't know much about spirits. I live in my dreams — that's what you sense. Other people live in dreams, but not in their own. That's the difference."

"Yes, maybe that's the way it is," he whispered. "It doesn't matter what kinds of dreams they are **in which** you live. — Have you heard about white magic?"

I had to say no.

"That is when you learn self-control. You can become immortal 불멸의 and bewitch people. Have you ever practiced any exercises?"

After I had inquired what these "exercises" were he became very secretive 숨기는; that is, until I turned to go back. Then he told me everything.

"For instance, when I want to fall asleep or want to concentrate on something I do one of these exercises. I think of something, a word for example, or a name or a geometrical form 기하학적 형태. Then I think this form into myself as hard as I can. I try to imagine it until I can actually feel it inside my head. Then I think it in the throat, and so forth, until I am completely filled by it. Then I'm as firm as though I had turned to stone and nothing can distract me any more."

I had a vague idea of what he meant. Yet I felt certain that there was something else troubling him, he was so strangely excited and restless. I tried to make it easy for him to speak, and it was not long before he expressed his real concern.

"You're continent, too, aren't you?" he asked reluctantly. "What do you mean, sexually?"

"Yes. I've been continent for two years — ever since I

seeker 구도자

maybe that's the way it is
아마 그럴지도 몰라
in which ~한 곳에서
white magic 치료, 구제
따위의 선행을 목적으로 하는
선의의 마술, 흑마술의 반대

bewitch ~에게 마법을 걸다

be filled by
~에 의해 채워지다

turn to=change into
distract 주의를 분산시키다

not long before ~
머지않아 ~하다

continent
대륙, 여기서는 금욕하는

- 128 -

found out about the exercises. I had been depraved 타락한
until then, you know what I mean. — So you've never
been with a woman?"

"No," I said. "I never found the right one."

"But if you did find a woman that you felt was the
right one, would you sleep with Her?"

관계대명사+(삽입구)+동사:
that (you felt) was the

"Yes, naturally — if she had no objections 반대," I said a
little derisively 조롱하듯.

"Oh, you're on the wrong path altogether! You can
train your inner powers only if you're completely
continent. I've been — for two whole years. Two years
and a little more than a month! It's so difficult!
Sometimes I think I can't stand it much longer."

stand=endure 견디다

"Listen, Knauer, I don't believe that continence 금욕 is
all that important."

"I know," he objected. "That's what they all say. But I
didn't expect you to say the same thing. If you want to
take the higher, the spiritual road you have to remain
absolutely pure."

"Well, be pure then! But I don't understand why
someone is supposed to be more pure than another
person if he suppresses 억제하다 his sexual urges. Or are
you capable of eliminating 제거하다 sex from all your
thoughts and dreams?"

be supposed to ~해야 한다,
~하기로 되어 있다.

be capable of ~ing
=be able to

He looked at me despairingly 절망하여.

"No, that's just the point. My God, but I have to. I
have dreams at night that I couldn't even tell myself.
Horrible dreams."

I remembered what Pistorius had told me. But **much as**
I agreed with his ideas I could not pass them on. I was
incapable of giving advice that did not derive from my
own experience and which I myself did not have the
strength to follow. I fell silent and felt humiliated at

much as ~한 만큼

pass them on
그의 말(ideas)을 전하다
derive from ~에서 나오다

feel humiliated
~에 굴욕감을 느끼다

being unable to give advice to someone who was seeking it from me.

"I've tried everything!" moaned Knauer beside me. "I've done everything there is to do. Cold water, snow, physical exercise and running, but nothing helps. Each night I awake from dreams that I'm not even allowed to think about — and the horrible part is that in the process I'm gradually forgetting everything spiritual I ever learned. I hardly ever succeed any more in concentrating or in making myself fall asleep. Often I lie awake the whole night. It can't go on much longer like this. If I can't win the struggle, if in the end I give in and become impure again, I'll be more wicked than all the others who never put up a fight. You understand that, don't you?"

I nodded but was unable to make any comment. He began to bore me and I was startled that his evident need and despair made no deeper impression on me. My only feeling was: I can't help you.

"So you don't know anything?" he finally asked sadly and exhausted 몹시 지친. "Nothing at all? But there must be a way. How do you do it?"

"I can't tell you anything, Knauer. We can't help anybody else. No one helped me either. You have to come to terms with yourself and then you must do what your inmost heart desires. There is no other way. If you can't find it yourself you'll find no spirits either."

The little fellow looked at me, disappointed and suddenly bereft of speech. Then his eyes flashed with hatred, he grimaced and shrieked: "Ah, you're a fine saint! You're depraved yourself, I know. You pretend to be wise but secretly you cling to the same filth the rest of us do! You're a pig, a pig, like me. All of us are

make ~ fall asleep

It can't ~ this. 이와 같은 방식이 오래 지속될 수는 없어.

put up=begin=try 시작하다

bore ~를 지루하게 만들다

come to terms with ~ ~를 받아들이는 것을 배우다

(being) bereft of speech 실망하여 갑자기 말을 잃고
grimace 얼굴을 찡그리다
shriek 소리를 지르다
depraved 타락한

filth (that) the rest of ~
filth 외설, 추잡한 짓

pigs!"

I went off and left him standing there. He followed me two or three steps, then turned around and ran away. I felt nauseated with pity and disgust 혐오 and the feeling did not leave me until I had surrounded myself with several paintings back in my room and surrendered to my own dreams. Instantly the dream returned, of the house entrance and the coat of arms, of the mother and the strange woman, and I could see her features **so** distinctly 뚜렷하게 **that** I began painting her picture that same evening.

When the painting was completed after several days' work, sketched out in dreamlike fifteen-minute spurts, I pinned it on the wall, moved the study lamp in front of it, and stood before it as though before a ghost **with which** I had had to struggle to the end. It was a face similar to the earlier one ─ a few features 특징 even resembled me. One eye was noticeably higher than the other and the gaze went over and beyond me, self-absorbed and rigid, full of fate.

I stood before it and began to freeze inside from the exertion. I questioned the painting, berated it, made love to it, prayed to it; I called it mother, called it whore 창녀 and slut, called it my beloved, called it Abraxas. Words said by Pistorius ─ or Demian? ─ occurred to me between my imprecations 욕설. I could not remember who had said them but I felt I could hear them again. They were words about Jacob's wrestling with the angel of God and his "I will not let thee go except thou bless me."

The painted face in the lamplight changed with each exhortation ─ became light and luminous 빛나는, dark and brooding, closed pale eyelids over dead eyes, opened them again and flashed lightning glances 눈짓. It was

feel nauseated
메스꺼움/역겨움을 느끼다

surrender to
~에 빠지다, 열중하다

so ~ that 구조

in dreamlike ~ spurts
15분간의 격정적인 붓놀림으로

struggle with ~ to the end
~와 끝까지 싸우다

the gaze ~ me 시선은 나를 넘어서서 어딘가로 향하다
self-absorbed 자기 생각에 몰두/전념한
freeze inside ~ exertion 긴장하여 내면이 싸늘해지다
exertion 노력, 노고, 진력
berate 호되게 꾸짖다

slut 암캐, 더러운 여자

them=the words

with each exhortation
각각의 훈계/권고에 따라서

brooding 생각에 잠긴

woman, man, girl, a little child, an animal, it dissolved into a tiny patch of color, grew large and distinct again. Finally, following a strong impulse 충동, I closed my eyes and now saw the picture within me, stronger and mightier than before. I wanted to kneel down before it but it was **so** much a part of me **that** I could not separate it from myself, as though it had been transformed into my own ego.

Then I heard a dark, heavy roaring 부르짖음 as if just before a spring storm and I trembled with an indescribable 형언할 수 없는 new feeling of fearful experience. Stars flashed up before me and died away: memories as far back as my earliest forgotten childhood, yes, even as far back as my pre-existence at earlier stages of evolution 진화, thronged past me. But these memories that seemed to repeat every secret of my life to me did not stop with the past and the present. They went beyond it, mirroring the future, tore me away from the present into new forms of life whose images shone blindingly clear — not one could I clearly remember later on.

During the night I awoke from deep sleep: still dressed I lay diagonally 대각선으로 across the bed. I lit the lamp, felt that I had to recollect something important but could not remember anything about the previous hour. Gradually I began to have an inkling. I looked for the painting — it was no longer on the wall, nor on the table either. Then I thought I could dimly remember that I had burned it. Or had this been in my dream that I burned it in the palm of my hand and swallowed the ashes?

A great restlessness 불안감 overcame me. I put on a hat and walked out of the house through the alley as though compelled, ran through innumerable 무수한 streets and squares as though driven by a frenzy 광기, listened briefly

dissolve into
~로 분해/해체되다

so ~ that 구조

be transformed into
~로 변형되다

memories ~ thronged past me 추억들이 밀려와 흘러갔다
as far back as ~ 만큼 멀리 떨어진 곳으로부터의 기억들

these memories ~ did not stop

tear A from B into C:
A를 B로부터 떼어내어 C가 되게 하다
blindingly clear 명확한
부정어 도치구조:
not one *could I remember*

have an inkling of ~에 대해 어렴풋이 기억나다

this=that ~ ashes

(주어+be) 생략 구조:
as though (I was) compelled ~ 강요당한 듯
as though (I was) driven by ~에 의해 내몰린 듯

in front of my friend's dark church, searched, searched
with extreme urgency — without knowing what. I walked
through a quarter with brothels 매춘굴 where I could still
see here and there a lighted window. Farther on I
reached an area of newly built houses, with piles of
bricks everywhere partially covered with gray snow. I
remembered — as I drifted under the sway of some
strange compulsion like a sleepwalker through the streets
— the new building back in my home town **to which** my
tormentor Kromer had taken me for my first payment.

A similar building stood before me now in the gray
night, its dark entrance **yawning** at me. It drew me
inside: wanting to escape I stumbled over sand and
rubbish 쓰레기. The power that drove me was stronger: I
was forced to enter. Across boards and bricks I
stumbled into a dreary 음산한 room that smelled moist and
cold from fresh cement. There was a pile of sand, a
light-gray patch, otherwise it was dark. Then a horrified
voice called out: "My God, Sinclair, where did you come
from?" Beside me a figure rose up out of the darkness, a
small lean fellow, like a ghost, and even in my terror I
recognized my fellow student Knauer.

"How did you happen to come here?" he asked, mad
with excitement. "How were you able to find me?"

I didn't understand. "I wasn't looking for you," I said,
benumbed. Each word meant a great effort and came
only haltingly, through dead lips.

He stared at me. "Weren't looking for me?" "No.
Something drew me. Did you call me? You must have
called me. What are you doing here anyway? It's night."

He clasped me convulsively with his thin arms. "Yes,
night. Morning will soon be here. Can you forgive me?"

"Forgive you what?"

with extreme urgency
매우 긴급하게
quarter=district 구역

drift ~ a sleepwalker
몽유병 환자처럼 이상한
충동에 이끌려 돌아다니다
compulsion 욕망, 충동
take A to B:
A를 B에 데리고 가다
tormentor 괴롭히는 자

주어+분사구: 그리고 ~하다
yawn 크게 입을 벌리다
stumble over
~위로 넘어질 뻔하다

stumble into
비틀거리며 ~로 들어가다

light-gray patch
연회색 지역, 부분

benumbed 어리둥절한 상태로
come haltingly
더듬더듬 나오다

clasp me convulsively
발작적으로 나를 끌어안다

"Oh, I was so awful."

Only now I remembered our conversation. Had that been only four, five days ago?

A whole lifetime seemed to have passed since then. But suddenly I knew everything. Not only what had transpired 발생하다 between us but also why I had come here and what Knauer had wanted to do out here.

not only A but also B
transpire=happen=occur

"You wanted to commit suicide, Knauer?"

He trembled with cold and fear.

"Yes, I wanted to. I don't know whether I would have been able to. I wanted to wait until morning."

I drew him into the open. The first horizontal rays of daylight glimmered cold and listless in the gray dawn.

horizontal rays of daylight
수평으로 비치는 햇살
glimmer 희미하게 빛나다

For a while I led the boy by the arm. I heard myself say: "Now go home and don't say a word to anyone! You were on the wrong path. We aren't pigs as you seem to think, but human beings. We create gods and struggle with them, and they bless us."

We walked on and parted company without saying another word. When I reached the house, it was already daylight.

part company 헤어지다

The best things I gained from my remaining weeks in St. ――― were the hours spent with Pistorius at the organ or in front of his fire. We were studying a Greek text about Abraxas and he read me extracts from a translation of the Vedas and taught me how to speak the sacred "om." Yet these occult matters were not what nourished me inwardly. What invigorated me was the progress I had made in discovering my self, the increasing confidence in my own dreams, thoughts, and intimations 암시, and the growing knowledge of the power I possessed within me.

extracts 발췌한 글

베다: 옛 인도의 성전

om: 옴, 힌두교 등에서 의식
전후에 말하는 신성한 소리
nourish 자양분을 주다
invigorate 원기/활기를 주다

Pistorius and I understood each other in every possible

way. All I had to do was think of him and I could be certain that he — or a message from him — would come. I could ask him anything, as I had asked Demian, without his having to be present in the flesh: all I had to do was visualize him and direct my questions at him in the form of intensive thought. Then all psychic effort expended on the question would return to me in kind, as an answer. Only **it was** not the person of Pistorius nor that of Max Demian **that** I conjured up and addressed, but the picture I had dreamed and painted, the half-male, half-female dream image of my daemon. This being was now no longer confined to my dreams, no longer merely depicted on paper, but lived within me as an ideal and intensification 강화 of my self.

The relationship which the would-be suicide Knauer formed with me was peculiar, occasionally even funny. Ever since the night in which I had been sent to him, he clung to me like a faithful servant or a dog, made every effort to forge his life with mine, and obeyed me blindly. He came to me with the most astonishing 놀라운 questions and requests, wanted to see spirits, learn the cabala, and would not believe me when I assured him that I was totally ignorant in all these matters. He thought nothing was beyond my powers. Yet it was strange that he would often come to me with his fanciful notions and requests frequently provided a catchword and the impetus for a solution. Often he was a bother and I would dismiss him peremptorily; yet I sensed that he, too, had been sent to me, that from him, too, came back whatever I gave him, in double measure; he, too, was a leader for me -- or at least a guidepost. The occult books and writings he brought me and in which he sought his salvation taught me more than I realized at the time.

without ~ be present
데미안이 곁에 없어도

psychic effort (which was)
extended on ~에 기울인
정신적 노력
in kind 마찬가지로

conjure up and address
맘에 떠올리고 말을 걸다
it was ~ that 강조 구문
not A, but B

be confined to ~에 제한되다

be depicted on
~위에 그려지다/표현되다

would-be suicide
자살을 할 뻔했던

forge=make

cabala 유대교 신비주의, 밀교

provide ~ a solution.
문제 해결을 위한 실마리나
계기(힘)를 제공하다
dismiss him peremptorily
단호하게 그의 말을 무시하다

come back ~ measure
내가 준 것이 무엇이건
두 배가 되어 되돌아오다

guidepost 이정표, 길잡이

The occult books ~ taught
신비주의, 비교에 관한 책

Later Knauer slipped unnoticed out of my life. We never came into conflict with each other; there was no reason to. Unlike Pistorius, with whom I was still to share a strange experience toward the end of my days in St. -------. On one or on several occasions in the course of their lives, even the most harmless people do not altogether escape coming into conflict with the fine virtues of piety and gratitude. Sooner or later each of us must take the step that separates him from his father, from his mentors; each of us must have some cruelly lonely experience -- even if most people cannot take much of this and soon crawl back. I myself had not parted from my parents and their world, the "luminous" world in a violent struggle, but had gradually and almost imperceptibly become estranged. I was sad that it had to be this way and it made for many unpleasant hours during my visits back home; but it did not affect me deeply, it was bearable 견딜만한.

But **where** we have given of our love and respect not from habit but of our own free will, **where** we have been disciples 제자 and friends out of our inmost hearts, it is a bitter and horrible moment when we suddenly recognize that the current within us wants to pull us away from what is dearest to us. Then every thought that rejects the friend and mentor turns in our own hearts like a poisoned barb, then each blow struck in defense flies back into one's own face, the words "disloyalty" 불성실 and "ingratitude" 배은망덕 strike the person who feels he was morally sound like catcalls and stigma 야유와 낙인, and the frightened heart flees timidly back to the charmed valleys of childhood virtues, unable to believe that this break, too, must be made, this bond also broken.

With time my inner feelings had slowly turned against

come into conflict with
~와 충돌하다
the fine ~ gratitude
경건과 감사라는 미덕

take much of this
이러한 혹독한 고독을 견디다
crawl back 몸을 숙이고
(이전으로) 되돌아가다

in a violent struggle
격렬하게 투쟁해도
imperceptibly ~ estranged.
나도 모르는 사이에 점차
소원해지다, 멀어지다
it had to ~ back home
늘 이런 식이어야 한다는
사실에 슬펐지만, 고향을
방문하는 동안 기분이 좋지
못할 때 아버지의 세계로 숨어
들어갔다.
where ~ 해왔던 곳에서
give of ~를 아낌없이 내주다
out of our inmost hearts
진정으로

current 흐름, 조류, 경향
pull us away from
우리를 ~로부터 떼어 놓다
reject 거절/거부하다
turn in ~를 향하다/찌르다
poisoned barb 독침
each blow ~ own face
(독침을 막아내려는) 방어의
타격이 오히려 자신의 얼굴을
향한다.
be morally sound like
~처럼 도덕적으로 건전하다
strike the person ~ like -
-처럼 ~한 사람을 두들겨 패다

charmed valley 마법의 계곡

- 136 -

acknowledging Pistorius so unreservedly as a master. My friendship with him, his counsel 조언, the comfort he had brought me, his proximity 친교 had been a vital experience during the most important months of my adolescence 사춘기. God had spoken to me through him. From his lips my dreams had returned clarified and interpreted. He had given me faith in myself. And now I became conscious of gradually beginning to resist him. There was too much didacticism in what he said, and I felt that he understood only a part of me completely.

No quarrel or scene occurred between us, no break and not even a settling of accounts. I uttered only a single -- actually harmless -- phrase, yet **it was** in that moment **that** an illusion was shattered.

A vague presentiment of such an occurrence had oppressed me for some time; it became a distinct feeling one Sunday morning in his study. We were lying before the fire while he was holding forth about mysteries and forms of religion, which he was studying, and whose potentialities 가능성 for the future preoccupied him. All this seemed to me odd and eclectic 절충적인 and not of vital importance; there was something vaguely pedagogical 교육적인 about it; it sounded like tedious 지루한 research among the ruins of former worlds. And all at once I felt a repugnance 반감 for his whole manner, for this cult of mythologies, this game of mosaics he was playing with secondhand modes of belief.

"Pistorius," I said suddenly in a fit of malice that both surprised and frightened me. "You ought to tell me one of your dreams again sometime, a real dream, one that you've had at night. What you're telling me there is all so -- so damned antiquarian 몹시 고리타분함."

He had never heard me speak like that before and at

turn against ~ a master
A를 스승으로 거리낌 없이
인정하는 데 반기를 들다

return ~~ interpreted
밝혀지고 해석 되어 돌아오다

didacticism 교훈적 경향

a settling of accounts
결산/관계의 청산 작업
it was ~ that 강조 구문

a vague ~ occurrence
그런 일이 생길 것이라는
막연한 예감

hold forth about
~에 대해 이야기를 나누다
whose possibilities
그것(신비나 종교의 형태)의
가능성

among ruins of
~의 폐허를 뒤지는

the game of mosaics
짜 맞추기 식의 게임
with secondhand ~ belief
간접적인 믿음의 방식으로

in a fit of malice
악의적인 말투로

the same moment I realized with a flash of shame and horror that the arrow I had shot at him, that had pierced his heart, had come from his own armory 무기창고: I was now flinging back 되던지다 at him reproaches 비난 that on occasion 때때로 he had directed against himself half in irony.

He fell silent at once. I looked at him with dread in my heart and saw him turning terribly pale.

After a long pregnant pause he placed fresh wood on the fire and said in a quiet voice: "You're right, Sinclair, you're a clever boy. I'll spare you the antiquarian stuff from now on." He spoke very calmly but it was obvious he was hurt. What had I done?

I wanted to say something encouraging to him, implore his forgiveness, assure him of my love and my deep gratitude. Touching words came to mind -- but I could not utter them. I just lay there gazing into the fire and kept silent. He, too, kept silent and so we lay while the fire dwindled, and with each dying flame I felt something beautiful, intimate irrevocably burn low and become evanescent.

"I'm afraid you've misunderstood me," I said finally with a very forced and clipped voice. The stupid, meaningless words fell mechanically from my lips as if I were reading from a magazine serial 잡지의 연재물.

"I quite understand," Pistorius said softly. "You're right." I waited. Then he went on slowly: "Inasmuch as one person can be right against another."

No, no! I'm wrong, a voice screamed inside me — but I could not say anything. I knew that with my few words I had put my finger on his essential weakness, his affliction 고통 and wound. I had touched the spot where he most mistrusted himself. His ideal way "antiquarian," he was seeking in the past, he was a romantic. And suddenly I realized deeply within me: what Pistorius had been and given to me was precisely what he could not be and give to himself. He had led me along a path that would transcend and leave even him, the leader, behind.

(Being) ~ antiquarian
그가 이상을 추구하는 방식이 좀 고리타분하긴 해도

He had led me ~ behind
그를 초월하여 그 자신마저도 뒤 처지게 만드는 길로 나를 이끌었다.

God knows how one happens to say something like that. I had not meant it all that maliciously 악의적으로, had had no idea of the havoc 대혼란 I would create. I had uttered something the implications 결과 of which I had been unaware of at the moment of speaking. I had succumbed to a weak, rather witty but malicious impulse 악의적인 충동 and it had become fate. I had committed a trivial and careless act of brutality 잔인한 행동 which he regarded as a judgment.

succumb to ~에 굴복하다

How much I wished then that he become enraged, defend himself, and berate me! He did nothing of the kind — I had to do all of that myself. He would have smiled if he could have, and the fact that he found it impossible was the surest proof of how deeply I had wounded him.

enraged=angry
berate=reproach harshly

By accepting this blow so quietly, from me, his impudent and ungrateful pupil, by keeping silent and admitting that I had been right, by acknowledging my words as his fate, he made me detest 혐오하다 myself and increased my indiscretion 경솔함 even more. When I had hit out I had thought I would strike a tough, well-armed man — he turned out to be a quiet, passive, defenseless creature who surrendered without protest.

impudent 건방진

ungrateful 감사할 줄 모르는

hit out 그런 말을 내뱉다

well armed 잘 무장된

turn out to be
~임이 판명되다

For a long time we stayed in front of the dying fire, in which each glowing shape 타오르는 모습, each writhing twig reminded me of our rich hours and increased the guilty awareness of my indebtedness 빚 to Pistorius. Finally I could bear it no longer. I got up and left. I stood a long

writhing twig
꺼져가는 모닥불(잔가지)
remind A of B:
A에게 B가 생각나게 하다

bear=endure=put up with
참다, 견디다

time in front of the door to his room, a long time on the dark stairway, and even longer outside his house waiting to hear if he would follow me. Then I turned to go and walked for hours through the town, its suburbs, parks and woods, until evening. During that walk I felt for the first time the mark of Cain on my forehead.

Only gradually was I able to think clearly about what had occurred. At first my thoughts were full of self-reproach 자책감, intent on **defending** Pistorius. But all of them turned into the opposite of my intention. A thousand times I was ready to regret and take back my rash statement 경솔한 말 — yet it had been the truth. Only now I managed to understand Pistorius completely and succeeded in constructing his whole dream before me. This dream had been to be a priest, to proclaim 선포하다 the new religion, to introduce new forms of exaltation 찬양, of love, of worship, to erect new symbols. But this was not his strength and it was not his function. He lingered too fondly in the past, his knowledge of this past was too precise 정확한, he knew too much about Egypt and India, Mithras and Abraxas. His love was shackled to images the earth had seen before, and yet, in his inmost heart, he realized **that** the New had to be truly new and different, **that** it had to spring from fresh soil and could not be drawn from museums and libraries. His function was perhaps to lead men to themselves as he had led me. To provide them with the unprecedented 전례 없는, the new gods, was not in him. At this point a sharp realization burned within me: each man has his "function" but none **which** he can choose himself, define, or perform as he pleases. It was wrong to desire new gods, completely wrong to want to provide the world with something. An enlightened man had but

suburbs 교외, 주택지구

the mark of Cain
카인의 표적
only 부사 도치 구조:
only gradually *was I able*

be intent on ~에 전념하다
(being) intent on defending
~를 옹호하고자 열중하면서

take back 거두어들이다

it=what I said to him

succeed in constructing ~
그의 모든 꿈을 내 앞에
그려내는데 성공하다

was not his strength ~
그의 힘으로 불가했고 그의
직무도 아니었다.
linger too fondly in
애정을 가지고 오래 머무르다
미트라(Mithras): 페르시아
신화의 빛과 진리의 신
be shackled to ~에 얽매이다

the New 새로운 것

it=the New

lead men to ~ 인간이 자기
자신의 길로 가도록 이끌다

function 역할, 임무
none which he can choose
그가 원하는 대로 선택하고
정의하고 수행할 임무는
지니고 있지 않다.
an enlightened man
각성한 자, 깨달은 자

one duty — to seek the way to himself, to reach inner certainty, to grope his way forward, no matter where it led. The realization shook me profoundly 심하게, it was the fruit of this experience. I had often speculated with images of the future, dreamed of roles that I might be assigned, perhaps as poet or prophet or painter, or something similar.

All that was futile. I did not exist to write poems, to preach or to paint, neither I nor anyone else. All of that was incidental 우연한. Each man had only one genuine vocation — to find the way to himself. He might end up as poet or madman, as prophet 예언자 or criminal — that was not his affair, ultimately it was of no concern. His task was to discover his own destiny 운명 — not an arbitrary one — and live it out wholly and resolutely within himself. Everything else was only a would-be existence, an attempt at evasion 회피, a flight back to the ideals of the masses 대중, conformity and fear of one's own inwardness 속마음. The new vision rose up before me, glimpsed a hundred times, possibly even expressed before but now experienced for the first time by me. I was an experiment on the part of Nature, a gamble within the unknown, perhaps for a new purpose, perhaps for nothing, and my only task was to allow this game on the part of primeval depths to take its course, to feel its will within me and make it wholly mine. That or nothing!

I had already felt much loneliness, now there was a deeper loneliness still which was inescapable.

I made no attempt at reconciliation 화해 with Pistorius. We remained friends but the relationship changed. Yet this was something we touched on only once; actually **it was** Pistorius alone **who** did. He said: "You know that I have the desire to become a priest. Most of all I wanted to become the priest of the new religion of which you and I have had so many intimations. That role will never be mine — I realize that and even without wholly admitting it to myself have known it for some time. So I will perform other priestly duties instead, perhaps at the organ, perhaps some other way. But I must always have things around me **that** I feel are beautiful and sacred, organ music and mysteries, symbols and myths.

I need and cannot forgo them. That is my weakness. Sometimes, Sinclair, I know that I should not have such wishes, that they are a weakness and luxury. **It** would be more magnanimous and just **if** I put myself unreservedly at the disposal of fate. But I can't do that, I am incapable of it. Perhaps you will be able to do it one day. It is difficult, it is the only truly difficult thing there is. I have often dreamed of doing so, but I can't; the idea fills me with dread: I am not capable of standing so naked and alone. I, too, am a poor weak creature who needs warmth and food and occasionally the comfort of human companionship 교제. Someone who seeks nothing but his own fate no longer has any companions 동료, he stands quite alone and has only cold universal space around him. That is Jesus in the Garden of Gethsemane, you know. There have been martyrs 순교자 who gladly let themselves be nailed to the cross, but even these were no heroes, were not liberated, for even they wanted something that they had become fond of and accustomed to — they had models, they had ideals. But the man who only seeks his destiny has neither models nor ideals, has nothing dear and consoling! And actually this is the path one should follow. People like you and me are quite lonely really but we still have each other, we have the secret satisfaction of being different, of rebelling, of

have an intimation of
~에 대해 암시/시사하다

주격 관/대 + 삽입구:
things that (I feel) are beautiful and sacred ~

forgo=give up

가주어 it, 진주어 if:
만약 ~한다면 더 관대하고 공정할 것이다
put ~ disposal of fate
거리낌 없이 운명의 처분에 내 자신을 맡기다

the only ~ there is 존재하는 것 중 유일한 진짜 어려운 일

nothing but=only

겟세마네 동산: 예루살렘의 감람산에 위치, 예수가 십자가 죽음을 앞두고 마지막 기도를 했던 동산

consoling 위안이 되는

남과 다르다는 점에서 오는 만족감

desiring the unusual. But you must shed that, too, if you want to go all the way to the end. You cannot allow yourself to become a revolutionary 혁명가, an example, a martyr. It is beyond imagining —"

Yes, it was beyond imagining. But it could be dreamed, anticipated, sensed. A few times I had a foretaste of it — in an hour of absolute stillness. Then I would gaze into myself and confront the image of my fate. Its eyes would be full of wisdom, full of madness, they would radiate love or deep malice 악의, it was all the same. You were not allowed to choose or desire any one of them. You were only allowed to desire yourself, only your fate. Up to this point, Pistorius had been my guide.

In those days I walked about as though I were blind. I felt frenzies 광기 — each step was a new danger. I saw nothing in front of me except the unfathomable darkness **into which** all paths I had taken until now had led and vanished. And within me I saw the image of the master, who resembled Demian, and in whose eyes my fate stood written.

I wrote on a piece of paper: "A leader has left me. I am enveloped in darkness. I cannot take another step alone. Help me."

I wanted to mail it to Demian, but didn't. Each time I wanted to, it looked foolish and senseless. But I knew my little prayer by heart and often recited it to myself. It was with me every hour of the day. I had begun to understand it.

My schooldays were over. I was to take a trip during my vacation — my father's idea — and then enter a university. But I did not know what I would major in. I had been granted my wish: one semester of philosophy. Any other subject would have done as well.

shed that 만족감을 버리다

have a foretaste of
~를 예감하다, 미리 맛보다

its eyes 운명의 눈
radiate 발산하다

up to this point
이 시점까지 오는 데

unfathomable darkness
깊이를 헤아릴 수 없는 어둠
lead into ~로 통하다
vanish into ~로 사라지다
stood written=was written

be enveloped in
~에 둘러싸여 있다

I had ~ my wish
나의 소망은 수용되었다.
I had granted *myself* my
wish. --> I had been
granted my wish.

Chapter VII
EVA

7. Eva

Once during my vacation I visited the house **where** years before Demian had lived with his mother. I saw an old woman strolling in the garden and, speaking with her, learned that it was her house. I inquired after the Demian family. She remembered them very well but could not tell me where they lived at present. Sensing my interest she took me into the house, brought out a leather album and showed me a photo of Demian's mother. I could hardly remember what she looked like, but now as I saw the small likeness my heart stood still: it was my dream image! That was she, the tall, almost masculine 남성적인 woman who resembled her son, with maternal traits 모성적 특징, severity 엄격, passion; beautiful and alluring 매혹적인, beautiful and unapproachable, daemon and mother, fate and beloved. There was no mistaking her!

To discover in this fashion that my dream image existed struck me as a miracle. So there was a woman who looked like that, who bore the features of my destiny! And to be Demian's mother. Where was she?

Shortly afterwards I embarked on my trip. What a strange journey it was! I traveled restlessly 들떠서 from place to place, following every impulse, always searching for this woman. There were days **when** everyone I met reminded me of her, echoed her, seemed to resemble her, drew me through the streets of unfamiliar cities, through railroad stations and into trams, as in an intricate 뒤얽힌 dream. There were other days **when** I realized the futility of my search. Then I would idly sit somewhere in a park or in some hotel garden, in a waiting room, trying to make the picture come alive

where=in which

inquire after
~의 안부를 묻다

my heart stood still
심장이 멎을 뻔하다

다이몬: 신과 인간 사이의 초자연적 존재, 수호신
There ~ her! 의심할 여지없이 바로 그녀였다.

in this fashion 이런 식으로
to discover ~ struck me
strike-struck

bear-bore-born 가지다

embark on=start, begin

days when: ~하던 날들

tram 시가 전차
futility=uselessness 헛됨

make ~ come alive

within me. But it had become shy and elusive. I found it impossible to fall asleep. Only while traveling on the train *could I catch* an occasional brief nap. Once, in Zurich 취리히, a woman approached me, an impudent pretty creature. I took hardly any notice of her and walked past as though she didn't exist. I would rather have died on the spot than have paid attention to another woman, even for an hour.

I felt my fate drawing me on, I felt the moment of my fulfillment coming near and I was sick with impatience 조급함 at not being able to do anything. Once in a railroad station, in Innsbruck I think, I caught sight of a woman who reminded me of her — in a train just pulling away. I was miserable for days. And suddenly the form reappeared in a dream one night. I awoke humiliated and dejected by the futility of my hunt and I took the next train home.

A few weeks later I enrolled at the university of H. I found everything disappointing. The lectures on the history of philosophy were just as uninspired 지루한 and stereotyped 상투적인 as the activities of most of the students. Everything seemed to run according to an old pattern, everyone was doing the same thing, and the exaggerated gaiety 과장된 쾌활함 on the boyish faces looked depressingly empty and ready-made. But at least I was free, I had the whole day to myself, lived quietly and peacefully in an old house near the town wall, and on my table lay a few volumes of Nietzsche. I lived with him, sensed the loneliness of his soul, perceived the fate that had propelled him on inexorably; I suffered with him, and rejoiced that there had been one man who had followed his destiny so relentlessly 가차 없이.

Late one evening I was sauntering through town. An

---

elusive 교묘히 잘 빠져나가는

only 부사절 도치구조:
only while ~ *could I catch*

impudent 건방진, 뻔뻔스러운

would rather A than B:
B 하느니 차라리 A 하는 게 더 낫다

지각동사+목+목/보(ing):
feel ~ drawing
feel~coming near

Innsbruck 인스브루크
오스트리아의 관광도시
pull away=leave

humiliated ~ my hunt
그녀를 찾아 헛되이 돌아다닌 것에 대해 수치를 느끼고 낙담하다

depressingly empty
맥 빠질 정도로 공허한
ready-made 기성품 같은

장소부사+동사 도치구조:
on my table *lay a few volumes*

니체: 독일의 작가, 철학자
힘에의 의지, 위버멘쉬,
영원회귀 사상을 주장

propel ~ on inexorably
무자비하게 계속 몰고 가다

saunter 어슬렁거리다

autumn wind was blowing and I could hear the
fraternities frolic in the taverns 술집. Clouds of tobacco
smoke drifted out open windows with a profusion of
song, loud, rhythmic yet uninspired, lifelessly uniform.

I stood at a street corner and listened: out of two bars
the methodically rehearsed gaiety of youth rang out
against the night. False communion 거짓 친교 everywhere,
everywhere shedding the responsibility of fate, flight to
the herd for warmth.

Two men slowly walked past behind me. I caught a few
words of their conversation.

"Isn't it just like the young men's house in a kraal?"
said one of them. "Everything fits down to the tattooing
which is in vogue again. Look, that's young Europe."

The voice sounded strangely and admonishingly 타이르듯
familiar. I followed the two of them down the dark lane.
One of them was a Japanese, small and elegant. Under a
street lamp I saw his yellow face light up in a smile.

The other was now speaking again.

"I imagine it's just as bad where you come from, in
Japan. People that don't follow the herd are rare
everywhere. There are some here too."

I felt a mixture of alarm and joy at each word. I knew
the speaker. It was Demian.

I followed him and the Japanese through the wind-swept
streets; listening to their conversation I relished the
sound of Demian's voice. It still had its familiar ring; the
same old beautiful certainty and calm had all their old
power over me. Now all was well. I had found him.

At the end of a street in the suburbs the Japanese
took his leave and unlocked his house door. Demian
retraced his steps, I had stopped and was waiting for
him in the middle of the street. I became very agitated

지각동사 hear ~ frolic
fraternity 남학생 사교클럽
frolic 들떠서 떠들다

a profusion of=a lot of

lifelessly uniform
활기 없이 한결 같은

methodically ~ youth
조직적으로 훈련된 젊은이들의
쾌활한 소리

shed 피하다, 벗어버리다
운명의 책임에 대한 회피
무리 속으로의 도피

kraal (원주민의) 울타리를 친
부락, (울타리로 두른) 오두막
fit down to ~와 일치하다
be in vogue 유행하다

see ~ light up

it's just ~ from
일본 (젊은이들의) 상황도
이곳과 다를 바 없다.

some 무리를 따르지 않는
사람

relish=enjoy

retrace one's steps
왔던 길을 되돌아가다
agitated=excited

- 147 -

as I saw him approach, upright, with elastic step, in a
brown rubber raincoat. He came closer without changing
his pace until he stopped a few steps in front of me.
Then he removed his hat and revealed his old
light-skinned face with the decisive mouth and the
peculiar brightness on his broad forehead.

with elastic step
탄력 있는 걸음걸이로

decisive mouth
단호한 입, 꽉 다문 입

"Demian," I called out.

He stretched out his hand.

"So, it's you, Sinclair! I was expecting you."

"Did you know I was here?"

"I didn't exactly know it but I definitely wished you
were. I didn't catch sight of you until this evening.
You've been following us for quite some time."

catch sight of=see=find

"Did you recognize me at once?"

"Of course. You've changed somewhat. But you have
the sign."

"The sign. What kind of sign?"

"We used to call it the mark of Cain earlier on — if
you can still remember. It's our sign. You've always had
it, that's why I became your friend. But now it has
become more distinct."

"I wasn't aware of that. Or actually, yes, once I painted
a picture of you, Demian, and was astonished that it also
resembled myself. Was that the sign?"

"That was it. It's good that you're here. My mother will
be pleased, too."

Suddenly I was frightened.

"Your mother? Is she here, too? But she doesn't know
me."

"But she knows about you. She will recognize you even
without my saying who you are. We've been in the dark
about you for a long time."

be in the dark about ~에
대하여 소식을 듣지 못하다

"I often wanted to write you, but it was no use. I've

known for some time that I would find you soon. I waited for it each day."

He thrust his arm under mine and walked along with me. An aura of calm surrounded him which affected me, too. Soon we were talking as we used to talk in the past. Our thoughts went back to our time in school, the Confirmation classes and also to that last unhappy meeting during my vacation. Only our earliest and closest bond, the Franz Kromer episode, was never mentioned.

Suddenly we found ourselves in the midst of a strange conversation touching on many ominous topics. **Picking up** where Demian left off in his conversation with the Japanese, we had discussed the life most of the students led, then came to something else, something that seemed to lie far afield. Yet in Demian's words an intimate connection became evident.

He spoke about the spirit of Europe and the signs of the times. Everywhere, he said, we could observe the reign of the herd instinct, nowhere freedom and love. All this false communion 거짓 친교 — from the fraternities to the choral societies 합창단 and the nations themselves — was an inevitable development, was a community born of fear and dread, out of embarrassment, but inwardly rotten, outworn 진부한, close to collapsing 붕괴.

"Genuine communion," said Demian, "is a beautiful thing. But what we see nourishing everywhere is nothing of the kind. The real spirit will come from the knowledge that separate individuals have of one another and for a time it will transform the world. The community spirit at present is only a manifestation 표현 of the herd instinct. Men fly into each other's arms because they are afraid of each other - the owners are for themselves, the

thrust 밀어 넣다

an aura of calm
평온한, 침착한 기운
used to ~하곤 했다

mention ~에 대해 언급하다

ominous 불길한, 나쁜 징조의
touch on ~에 대해 언급하다
picking up:
데미안이 ~와의 대화에서
중단한 부분을 선택하여

the life (which) most of ~

lie far afield 훨씬 벗어나다

the reign of the herd
instinct 집단충동의 힘
fraternity 남학생 사교클럽,
신념이 같은 사람들의 동호회

(관/대+be 동사) 생략구조:
community (which was)
born of fear and dread
~에서 태어난 공동체

close to collapsing
와해/붕괴가 임박한

what we see ~ the kind
도처에 만연한 것들은 그런
종류의 친교/연대가 아니다
the knowledge ~ another
개인이 서로에 대해서 가지는
인식 혹은 이해
it=the real spirit

집단충동: 어떤 집단의 일원이
되어 그 집단의 표준에 맞게
행동하거나 의견을 내고
싶다는 본능 또는 충동

workers for themselves, the scholars for themselves! And why are they afraid? You are only afraid if you are not in harmony with yourself. People are afraid because they have never owned up to themselves. A whole society composed of men afraid of the unknown within them! They all sense that the rules they live by are no longer valid 타당한, that they live according to archaic 낡은 laws — neither their religion nor their morality is in any way suited to the needs of the present. For a hundred years or more Europe has done nothing but study and build factories! They know exactly how many ounces of powder it takes to kill a man but they don't know how to pray to God, they don't even know how to be happy for a single contented hour. Just take a look at a student dive! Or a resort where the rich congregate 모이다. It's hopeless. Dear Sinclair, nothing good can come of all of this. These people who huddle together in fear are filled with dread and malice 악의, no one trusts 신뢰하다 the other. They hanker after ideals that are ideals no longer but they will hound the man to death who sets up a new one. I can feel the approaching conflict. It's coming, believe me, and soon. Of course it will not 'improve' the world. Whether the workers kill the manufacturers or whether Germany makes war on Russia will merely mean a change of ownership. But it won't have been entirely in vain. It will reveal the bankruptcy 파산 of present-day ideals, there will be a sweeping away 소탕 of Stone Age gods. The world, as it is now, wants to die, wants to perish 멸망하다 — and it will."

"And what will happen to us during this conflict?"

"To us? Oh, perhaps we'll perish in it. Our kind can be shot, too. Only we aren't done away with as easily as all that. Around what remains of us, around those of us

학자는 학자들끼리

own up to themselves
그들 자신을 온전히 인정하다
생략구조: society (that is) composed of men (are) afraid of the unknown ~
be composed of=consist of
~로 구성되다

be suited to ~에 적합하다

nothing but=only

power 화약

for a single contented hour
느긋한 한 시간 동안
dive=bar 싸구려 술집

huddle together 두려워 함께 모여 몸을 움츠리고 있는 사람

hanker after=long for
~를 갈망하다
hound A to death:
새로운 이상을 내세우는 사람을 죽음으로 몰아넣다

a change of ownership
소유권의 변화/이전

sweeping away 소탕, 없애기

perish=die

do away with ~를 제거하다,

우리 가운데 남아있는 것 주위로

who survive, the will of the future will gather. The will of humanity 인류, which our Europe has shouted down for a time with its frenzy of technology, will come to the fore again. And then **it** will become clear **that** the will of humanity is nowhere — and never was — identical with the will of present-day societies, states and peoples, clubs and churches. No, what Nature wants of man stands indelibly written in the individual, in you, in me. It stood written in Jesus, it stood written in Nietzsche. These tendencies 경향 — which are the only important ones and which, of course, can assume different forms every day — will have room to breathe **once** the present societies have collapsed."

It was late when we stopped in front of a garden by the river.

'This is where we live," said Demian. "You must come visit us soon. We've been waiting for you."

Elated I walked the long way home through a night which had now turned chill. Here and there students were reeling noisily to their quarters. I had often marked the contrast between their almost ludicrous gaiety and my lonely existence, sometimes with scorn, sometimes with a feeling of deprivation 박탈감. But never until today had I felt with as much calm and secret strength how little **it** mattered to me, how remote and dead this world was for me. I remembered civil servants 관리 in my home town, worthy old gentlemen **who** clung to the memories of their drunken university days as to keepsakes 기념품 from paradise and fashioned a cult of their "vanished" student years **as** poets or other romantics 낭만가 fashion their childhood. It was the same everywhere! Everywhere they looked for "freedom" and "luck" in the past, out of sheer dread of their present responsibilities and future

shout down with
~로 인해 소리가 묻혀버린
come to the fore 드러나다

가주어 it, 진주어 that

be identical with
~와 동일하다

너와 나 속에 지워지지 않게
영원히 쓰여 있다.
stand written in
~ 안에 적혀 있다

assume different forms
다른 형태를 띠다
접속사 once: 일단 ~하면

(Being) elated: 기쁜
마음으로, 의기양양해서서

reel ~ quarters 그들의
숙소/집을 향해 시끄럽게
비틀거리며 가다
mark the contrast between
A and B: A와 B 사이에
뚜렷한 대조를 느끼다.
ludicrous gaiety
우스꽝스러운 쾌활함
부정부사 도치구조:
never ~ *had I felt*
I felt how little it ~ to me
(이전의 세계)가 별로 중요하지
않다고 느꼈다.
gentlemen **who** clung to ~
and fashioned -:
~에 집착하고 -를 만들어 내던
신사들

out of sheer dread of ~에
대한 순전한 두려움 때문에

course. They drank and caroused for a few years and then they slunk away to become serious-minded 진지한 gentlemen in the service of the state. Yes, our society was rotten, and these student stupidities 어리석은 짓 were not so stupid, not so bad as a hundred other things.

By the time I reached my distant house and was preparing for bed, all these thoughts had vanished and my entire being *clung expectantly to* the great promise that this day had brought me. As soon as I wished, even tomorrow, I **was to** see Demian's mother. Let the students have their drunken orgies 탐닉 and tattoo their faces; the rotten world could await its destruction — for all I cared. I was waiting for one thing — to see my fate step forth in a new guise.

I slept deeply until late in the morning. The new day dawned for me like a solemn feast 장엄한 축제, the kind I had not experienced since childhood. I was full of a great restlessness 불안, yet without fear of any kind. I felt that an important day had begun for me and I saw and experienced the changed world around me, expectant, meaningful, and solemn; even the gentle autumn rain had its beauty and a calm and festive air full of happy, sacred music.

For the first time the outer world was perfectly attuned to the world within; it was a joy to be alive. No house, no shop window, no face disturbed me, everything was as it should be, without any of the flat, humdrum look of the everyday; everything was a part of Nature, expectant and ready to face its destiny with reverence. That was how the world had appeared to me in the mornings when I was a small boy, on the great feast days, at Christmas or Easter. I had forgotten that the world could still be so lovely. I had grown accustomed to

carouse 흥청거리다
slink away 슬금슬금 도망치다
slink-slunk-slunk

cling expectantly to
기대하며 ~에 매달리다

was to=would 예정
let ~ have and tattoo

see ~ step forth
나의 운명이 새로운 모습으로
다가오는 것을 보는 것이다

be attuned to
~와 조화/조율을 이루다

disturb 마음을 어지럽히다

flat, humdrum look
활기 없고 단조로운 모습

its=Nature's
reverence 존경, 경외

living within myself. I was resigned to the knowledge **that**
I had lost all appreciation of the outside world, **that** the
loss of its bright colors was an inseparable part of the
loss of my childhood, and **that**, in a certain sense, one
had to pay for freedom and maturity of the soul with the
renunciation 포기 of this cherished aura 소중한 기운. But now,
overjoyed, I saw that all this had only been buried or
clouded over and that **it** was still possible — even if you
had become liberated and had renounced 포기하다 your
childhood happiness — **to** see the world shine and **to**
savor 음미하다 the delicious thrill of the child's vision.

The moment came **when** I found my way back to the
garden at the edge of town **where** I had taken leave of
Demian the night before. Hidden behind tall, wet trees
stood a little house, bright and livable. Tall plants
flowered behind plate glass 판유리; behind glistening
windows dark walls shone with pictures and rows of
books. The front door led straight into a small, warm
hallway. A silent old maid, dressed in black with a white
apron, showed me in and took my coat.

She left me alone in the hallway. I looked around and
at once was swept into the middle of my dream. High up
on the dark wood-paneled wall, above a door, hung a
familiar painting, my bird with the golden-yellow sparrow
hawk's head, clambering out of the terrestrial shell.
Deeply moved, I stood there motionless — I felt joy and
pain as though at this moment everything I had ever
done and experienced returned to me in the form of a
reply and fulfillment 성취. In a flash I saw hosts of images
throng past my mind's eye: my parents' house with the
old coat of arms above the doorway, the boy Demian
sketching the emblem, myself as a boy under the fearful
spell of my enemy Kromer, myself as an adolescent 청년

동격의 that 3개
be resigned to ~라는 사실을
기꺼이 받아들이다
appreciation 진가의 인식

pay for A with B:
B로 A의 대가를 지불하다

가주어 it, 진주어 to see and
to savor 보고 음미하는 것이
여전히 가능하다

see ~ shine

the moment came *when*:
~하는 순간이 왔다

관계부사 where=in which
take leave of ~와 헤어지다
주격보어 도치구조: Hidden ~
stood a little house

glistening=shining 반짝이는

be swept ~ my dream
내 꿈/환상 속으로 휩쓸려
들어가다

clambering out of
~에서 벗어나려고 애쓰면서
terrestrial shell
이 세상의 껍질
everything (that) I had

in a flash 순식간에
see ~ throng past ~가 때를
지어 지나가는 것을 보다

emblem 문장: 집안/가문을
나타내기 위한 상징적인
그림이나 모형

in my room at school painting my dream bird at a quiet table, the soul caught in the intricacies of its own threads — and everything, everything to this present moment resounded once more within me, was affirmed by me, answered, sanctioned 인정하다.

With tears in my eyes I stared at my picture and read within myself. Then I lowered my eyes: beneath the painting of the bird in the open door stood a tall woman in a dark dress. It was she.

I was unable to utter a word. With a face that resembled her son's, timeless, ageless, and full of inner strength, the beautiful woman smiled with dignity 품위. Her gaze was fulfillment 실현, her greeting a homecoming 귀향. Silently I stretched my hands out to her. She took both of them in her firm, warm hands.

"You are Sinclair. I recognized you at once. Welcome!"

Her voice was deep and warm. I drank it up like sweet wine. And now I looked up and into her quiet face, the black unfathomable eyes, at her fresh, ripe lips, the clear, regal brow that bore the sign.

"How glad I am," I said and kissed her hands. "I believe I have been on my way my whole life — and now I have come home."

She smiled like a mother.

"One never reaches home," she said. "But where paths that have affinity for each other intersect the whole world looks like home, for a time."

She was expressing what I had felt on my way to her. Her voice and her words resembled her son's and yet were quite different. Everything was riper, warmer, more self-evident. But just as Max had never given anyone the impression of being a boy, so his mother did not appear at all like a woman who had a full-grown son, so young

the soul (which was) caught in ~ threads
자신의 실로 짠 복잡한 것들에 사로잡힌 영혼
to this present moment
지금 이 순간 까지
resound 다시 울리다

unfathomable eyes
깊이를 헤아릴 수 없는 눈
regal brow ~ sign (카인의)
표적을 가진 당당한 눈썹

where paths ~ looks like
서로에 대해 마음이 끌리는 길들이 교차하는 곳은 ~처럼 보이다

just as A, so B:
꼭 A한 것처럼 B도 그러하다
appear like=look like

and sweet were her face and hair, so taut 팽팽한 and smooth her golden skin, so fresh her mouth. More regal 당당한 even than in my dreams she stood before me.

This, then, was the new guise 모습 in which my fate revealed itself to me, no longer stern 가혹한, no longer setting me apart, but fresh and joyful! I made no resolutions 결심, took no vows 맹세 — I had attained a goal, a high point on the road: from there the next stage of the journey appeared unhampered and marvelous, leading toward promised lands. Whatever might happen to me now, I was filled with ecstasy 환희: **that** this woman existed in the world, **that** I could drink in her voice and breathe her presence. No matter whether she would become my mother, my beloved or a goddess -- if she could just be here! if only my path would be close to hers!

She pointed up to my painting.

"You never made Max happier than with this picture," she said thoughtfully. "And me, too. We were waiting for you and when the painting came we knew that you were on your way. When you were a little boy, Sinclair, my son one day came home from school and said to me: there is a boy in school, he has the sign on his brow, he has to become my friend. That was you. You have not had an easy time but we had confidence in you. You met Max again during one of your vacations. You must have been about sixteen at the time. Max told me about it."

I interrupted: "He told you about that? That was the most miserable period of my life!"

"Yes, Max said to me: Sinclair has the most difficult part coming now. He's making one more attempt to take refuge among the others. He's even begun going to bars.

형용사보어 도치구조:
so young and sweet *were her face and hair*
보어도치+be 동사 생략구조:
-so taunt and smooth *(was) her golden skin*
-so fresh *(was) her mouth*

set A apart from B:
A를 B와 분리시키다

unhampered 제약받지 않는
marvelous 기적적인, 최고의

동격의 that: ecstasy that

no matter whether A or B:
A이든 B이든 상관없이

the sign 카인의 표식

But he won't succeed. His sign is obscured 흐려진 but it sears him secretly. Wasn't it like that?"

"Yes, exactly. Then I found Beatrice and I finally found a master again. His name was Pistorius. Only then did it become clear to me why my boyhood had been so closely bound up with Max and why I could not free myself from him. Dear mother, at that time I often thought that I should have to take my life. Is the way as difficult as this for everybody?"

She stroked my hair. The touch felt as light as a breeze.

"It is always difficult to be born. You know the chick does not find it easy to break his way out of the shell. Think back and ask yourself: Was the way all that difficult? Was it only difficult? Wasn't it beautiful, too? Can you think of a more beautiful and easier way?"

I shook my head.

"It was difficult," I said as though I were asleep, "it was hard until the dream came."

She nodded and pierced me with a glance.

"Yes, you must find your dream, then the way becomes easy. But there is no dream that lasts forever, each dream is followed by another, and one should not cling to any particular one."

I was startled and frightened. Was that a warning, a defensive 방어적 gesture, so soon? But it didn't matter: I was prepared to let her guide me and not to inquire into goals.

"I do not know," I said, "how long my dream is supposed to last. I wish it could be forever. My fate has received me under the picture of the bird like a lover and like a beloved. I belong to my fate and to no one else."

won't succeed (in taking refuges among the others)
sear him secretly
아무도 모르게 그를 불태우다

only then 도치구조:
only then *did it become*

be closely bound up with
~와 밀접한 관계가 있다

take one's life
=commit suicide

다시 태어나는 것은 어렵다.
죽음/파괴/고통이 있어야
새로운 창조가 있기 때문이다.

pierce me with a glance
뚫어지게 나를 쳐다보았다.

cling to ~를 고집/집착하다

that 내가 놀란 행위

let ~ guide me
be prepared not to inquire
~에 대해 샅샅이 캐묻지 않을
준비가 되다

be supposed to
~하기로 되어있다

I belong to my fate.
내 운명의 주인은 나다.

"As long as the dream is your fate you should remain faithful to it," she confirmed in a serious tone of voice.

I was overcome by sadness and a longing to die in this enchanted hour. I felt tears - what an infinity since I had last wept -- well up irresistibly in my eyes and overwhelm me. I turned abruptly away from her, stepped to the window, and stared blindly into the distance. I heard her voice behind me, calm and yet brimful with tenderness as a beaker with wine 술잔처럼.

"Sinclair, you are a child! Your fate loves you. One day it will be entirely yours -just as you dream it — if you remain constant to it."

I had gained control of myself and turned toward her again. She gave me her hand.

"I have a few friends," she said with a smile, "a few very close friends who call me Frau Eva. You shall be one of them if you wish."

She led me to the door, opened it, and pointed into the garden. "You'll find Max out there."

I stood dazed and shaken under the tall trees, not knowing whether I was more awake or more in a dream than ever. The rain dripped gently from the branches. Slowly I walked out into the garden that extended some way along the river. Finally I found Demian. He was standing in an open summer house, **stripped** to the waist, **punching** a suspended sandbag.

I stopped, astonished. Demian looked strikingly handsome with his broad chest, and firm, manly features; the raised arms with taut muscles were strong and capable 민첩한, the movements sprang playfully and smoothly from hips, shoulders, and wrists.

"Demian," I called out. "What are you doing there?"

He laughed happily.

remain faithful to
~에 충실하다
confirm 확인하다, 확신하다

enchanted 마법에 걸린
what an infinity since ~
얼마나 긴 시간이 흘렀든가!
felt tears well up ~
눈물을 참을 수 없을 정도로
샘솟는 것을 느끼다

brimful with ~로 넘쳐나는

remain constant to
~에 충실하다

stand dazed and shaken
멍한 혼돈스런 상태로 서 있다

(being) stripped
윗도리를 벌거벗은 채
punching ~ sandbag
매달린 샌드백을 치며

taut muscles 멋진 근육

- 157 -

"Practicing. I've promised the Japanese a boxing match, the little fellow is as agile 민첩한 as a cat and, of course, just as sly, but he won't be able to beat me. There's a very slight humiliation 굴욕 for which I have to pay him back."

He put on his shirt and coat.

"You've seen my mother?" he asked.

"Yes, Demian, what a wonderful mother you have! Frau Eva! The name fits her perfectly. She is like a universal mother."

For a moment he looked thoughtfully into my face.

"So you know her name already? You can be proud of yourself. You are the first person she has told it to during the first meeting."

From this day on I went in and out of the house like a son or brother — but also as someone in love. As soon as I opened the gate, as soon as I caught sight of the tall trees in the garden, I felt happy and rich. Outside was reality: streets and houses, people and institutions, libraries and lecture halls — but here inside was love; here lived the legend and the dream. And yet we lived in no way **cut off** from the outside world; in our thoughts and conversations we often lived in the midst of it, only on an entirely different plane. We were not separated from the majority of men by a boundary 경계 but simply by another mode of vision. Our task was to represent an island in the world, a prototype 표준 perhaps, or at least a prospect 전망 of a different way of life. I, who had been isolated for so long, learned about the companionship 교제 which is possible between people who have tasted complete loneliness. I never again hankered after the tables of the fortunate and the feasts of the blessed. Never again did envy or nostalgia overcome me when I

just as sly, but ~
영리할 만큼 민첩하지만

universal mother
만인/만물의 어머니

in no way=never
(being) cut off:
~와 단절된 채

only on ~ different plane
전적으로 다른 차원에서

mode of vision 보는 방식
represent 재현하다

hander after=longed for
갈망/동경하다
the fortunate 운이 좋은 자들
never *did envy overcome*
nostalgia 과거에 대한 동경

witnessed the collective pleasures of others. And gradually I was initiated into the secret of those who wear the sign in their faces.

We who wore the sign might justly be considered "odd" by the world; yes, even crazy, and dangerous. We were aware or in the process of becoming aware and our striving was directed toward achieving a more and more complete state of awareness **while** the striving 노력 of the others was a quest aimed at binding 구속하다 their opinions, ideals, duties, their lives and fortunes more and more closely to those of the herd 군중. There, too, was striving, there, too, were power and greatness. But **whereas** we, who were marked, believed that we represented the will of Nature to something new, to the individualism 개성 of the future, the others sought to perpetuate the status quo. Humanity — which they loved as we did — was for them something complete **that** must be maintained and protected. For us, humanity was a distant goal **toward which** all men were moving, **whose** image no one knew, **whose** laws were nowhere written down.

Apart from Frau Eva, Max, and myself, various other seekers were more or less closely attached to the circle. Quite a few had set out on very individual paths, had set themselves quite unusual goals, and clung to specific ideas and duties. They included astrologers and cabalists, also a disciple of Count Tolstoi, and all kinds of delicate, shy, and vulnerable creatures, followers of new sects, devotees 신봉자 of Indian asceticism, vegetarians, and so forth. We actually had no mental bonds in common save the respect [in] **which** each one accorded the ideals of the other. Those **with whom** we felt a close kinship were concerned with mankind's past search for gods and ideals — their studies often reminded me of Pistorius.

be initiated into
~를 전수받다
initiate 시작하다, ~ 전수하다

be directed toward
~로 향하다
while=whereas 반면에

a quest (which was) aimed
at ~를 목표로 하는 탐색
bind A to B:
A를 B에 구속시키다
those=lives and fortunes

represent A to B:
B에게 A를 제시하다

perpetuate the status quo
현재의 상태를 영속시키다
humanity 인류, 인간성, 인간애

something (which is)
complete 완전한 어떤 것

whose=and humanity's

apart from ~외에도
the circle of seekers
more or less 어느 정도

quite a few 상당수가
set out on ~ paths
개개의 독특한 길을 나서다

astrologer 점성술사
cabalist 히브리 신비주의자
disciple of Count Tolstoi
톨스토이 백작의 제자, 신봉자
vulnerable creatures
상처받기 쉬운 사람들
Indian asceticism
인도 금욕주의, 고행주의
have a bond in common
공통적인 유대를 가지다
save the respect
~한 사항을 제외하고
accord 따뜻이 맞아들이다

be concerned with
~와 관련이 있다

They brought books with them, translated aloud texts in ancient languages, showed us illustrations of ancient symbols and rites 의례 and taught us to see how humanity's entire store 저장 of ideals so far consisted of dreams **that** had emanated from the unconscious, of dreams **in which** humanity groped after its intimations of future potentialities. Thus we became acquainted with the wonderful thousand-headed tangle of gods from prehistory to the dawn 시작 of the Christian conversion. We heard the creeds of solitary holy men, of the transformations religions undergo in their migrations from one people to another. Thus, from everything we collected in this manner, we gained a critical 비판적인 understanding of our time and of contemporary Europe: with prodigious 엄청난 efforts, mighty new weapons had been created for mankind but the end was flagrant 혹심한, deep desolation 황폐 of the spirit. Europe had conquered the whole world only to lose her own soul.

Our circle also included believers, adherents 지지자 of certain hopes and healing faiths. There were Buddhists who sought to convert Europe, a disciple 신봉자 of Tolstoi who preached non-resistance 무저항 to evil, as well as other sects 종파. We in the inner circle listened but accepted none of these teachings as anything but metaphors. We, who bore the mark, felt no anxiety about the shape the future was to take. All of these faiths and teachings seemed to us already dead and useless. The only duty and destiny we acknowledged was **that** each one of us should become so completely himself, so utterly faithful to the active seed which Nature planted within him, **that** in living out its growth he could be surprised by nothing unknown to come.

Although we might not have been able to express it,

---

how A consist of B:
어떻게 A가 B를 구성하는 지
emanate from
~에서 발산하다
in which=where 그 꿈속에서
grope after ~를 모색하다
its intimations of 미래의
잠재적 가능성에 대한 암시
be acquainted with
~에 정통하다, 잘 알게 되다
천개의 머리가 얽힌 신들
tangle of gods 뒤얽힌 신들
conversion 전환, 개종
creed 교리, 신조, 신념
목적격 관/대 that 생략:
transformations (that)
religions undergo in ~에서
종교가 겪은 변화
migration 이주, 이전, 이동
everything (that) we
collected 우리가 모은 모든 것

A only to B:
A 했으나 결국 B 하다
our circle (of seekers)

convert 변화/개종시키다

as anything but metaphors
오직 상징으로써

접속사 that 2개: 보어역할

온전히 ~에 충실하다

그 씨앗이 성장하는 과정에
우리 각자는 다가올 미지의
것들에 의해 놀라지 않을 수
있었다.

we all felt distinctly that a new birth amid the collapse of this present world was imminent, already discernible. Demian often said to me: "What will come is beyond imagining. The soul of Europe is a beast that has lain fettered for an infinitely long time. And when it's free, its first movements won't be the gentlest. But the means are unimportant if only the real needs of the soul — which has for so long been repeatedly stunted and anesthetized — come to light. Then our day will come, then we will be needed. Not as leaders and lawgivers — we won't be there to see the new laws — but rather **as** those who are willing, as men who are ready to go forth and stand prepared wherever fate may need them. Look, all men are prepared to accomplish the incredible if their ideals are threatened. But no one is ready when a new ideal, a new and perhaps dangerous and ominous impulse, makes itself felt. The few who will be ready at that time and who will go forth — will be us. That is why we are marked — as Cain was — to arouse fear and hatred and drive men out of a confining idyll into more dangerous reaches. All men who have had an effect on the course of human history, all of them without exception, were capable and effective only because they were ready to accept the inevitable. It is true of Moses and Buddha, of Napoleon and Bismarck. What particular movement one serves and what pole one is directed from are matters outside one's own choice. If Bismarck **had understood** the Social Democrats and compromised with them he **would have** merely **been** shrewd but no man of destiny. The same applies to Napoleon, Caesar, Loyola, all men of that species in fact. Always, you must think of these things in evolutionary, in historical terms! 진화적, 역사적 면에서

imminent=impending 절박한, discernible 식별할 수 있는

a feast that has ~ fettered 속박당해 놓여 있는 짐승

means 수단, 방법

need 결핍, 부족, 곤궁

be stunted, anesthetized 저지되고, 마취되다
come to light 밝혀지다

then we will be needed 그때가 오면 우리의 역할이 필요할 것이다

go forth 전진하다
운명이 우리를 필요로 하는 곳 어디서든 준비된 자세로 서 있는 자로서
accomplish the incredible 믿기 어려운 일도 성취해 내다

when ominous impulse makes itself felt 불길한 충동이 느껴질 때
the few 극소수의 사람

arouse fear and hatred 공포와 증오를 불러일으키다
drive A out of B into C: A를 B에서 끌어내어 C로 이끌다
confining idyll 한정된/좁은 목가적 세계
have an effect on ~에 영향을 미치다

the inevitable 피할 수 없는 것들

비스마르크: 독일제국의 정치가

간접의문문 (의+주+동):
What ~ and what ~ from
be directed from ~로부터 지배를 받다
가정법 과거완료:
~했더라면, ~했을 텐데
shrewd 능수능란한
merely A but no B: 단순히 A이지 결코 B는 아니다
로욜라: 예수회의 창설자

fling A into B: fling-flung

When the upheavals 융기 of the earth's surface flung the creatures of the sea onto the land and the land creatures into the sea, the specimens of the various orders that were ready to follow their destiny were the ones that accomplished the new and unprecedented; by making new biological adjustments they were able to save their species from destruction. We do not know whether these were **the·same** specimens **that** had previously distinguished themselves among their fellows **as** conservative 보수주의자, upholders of the status quo 현상의 유지자, or rather **as** eccentrics 괴짜, revolutionaries 혁명가; but we do know they were ready, and could therefore lead their species into new phases of evolution. That is why we want to be ready."

Frau Eva was often present during these conversations yet she did not participate in quite the same manner. She was a listener, full of trust and understanding, an echo for each one of us who explained his thoughts. It seemed as though all thinking emanated from her and in the end went back to her. My happiness consisted in sitting near her, hearing her voice occasionally and sharing the rich, soulful atmosphere surrounding her.

She was immediately 즉각 aware of any change, any unhappiness or new development within me. It even seemed to me that my dreams at night were inspired by her. I would often recount them to her and she found them comprehensible 이해할 수 있는 and natural; there was no unusual turn in them that she could not follow. For a time my dreams repeated patterns of our daytime conversations. I dreamed that the whole world was in turmoil 동요 and that by myself, or with Demian, I was tensely waiting for the great moment. The face of fate remained obscured but somehow bore the features of

A를 B로 내던지다

다양한 종들의 표본들
specimen 표본

the ones=the specimens
새롭고 전례 없는 것들
by making ~ adjustments
생물학적 적응을 함으로써

the same A that B:
B를 했던 것과 동일한 표본(A)
previously ~ among
~가운데서 두각을 드러내다

전치사 as: ~로서

phases of evolution
진화의 단계

she=listener=echo 메아리

emanate from
~에서 발산하다
consist in ~에 있다

be inspired by
~에 의해 영감을 얻다
recount 자세히 얘기하다
=tell my dreams in detail

turn 특이한 전환/변화
them=my dreams

remain obscured
명백하지 않은 상태이다

Frau Eva: to be chosen or spurned by her, that was fate.

Sometimes she would say with a smile: "Your dream is incomplete, Sinclair. You've left out the best part."

And then I would remember the part I had left out and not understand how I could have forgotten it.

At times I was dissatisfied with myself and tortured with desire: I believed I could no longer bear to have her near me without taking her in my arms. She sensed this, too, at once. Once when I had stayed away for several days and returned bewildered she took me aside and said: "You must not give way to desires which you don't believe in. I know what you desire. You should, however, either be capable of renouncing these desires or feel wholly justified in having them. Once you are able to make your request in **such** a way **that** you will be quite certain of its fulfillment, then the fulfillment will come. But at present you alternate between desire and renunciation 포기 and are afraid all the time. All that must be overcome. Let me tell you a story."

And she told me about a youth who had fallen in love with a planet. He stood by the sea, stretched out his arms and prayed to the planet, dreamed of it, and directed all his thoughts to it. But he knew, or felt he knew, that a star cannot be embraced by a human being. He considered it to be his fate to love a heavenly body without any hope of fulfillment and out of this insight he constructed 세우다 an entire philosophy of renunciation 단념 and silent, faithful suffering **that** would improve and purify him. Yet all his dreams reached the planet. Once he stood again on the high cliff at night by the sea and gazed at the planet and burned with love for it. And at the height of his longing he leaped into the

be spurned by
~에 의해 퇴짜를 당하다

leave out 빠뜨리다
=omit=pass over

be tortured with desire
욕망으로 괴로워하다
bear=endure 견디다

return bewildered
(마음이) 혼란스러운 상태로
되돌아오다.
give way to ~에 굴복하다

renounce=give up
feel wholly justified in
~에 대해 전적으로 정당함을
느끼다
in such a way that:
~하게 될 그런 방식으로

alternate between A and B:
A와 B사이를 왔다 갔다 한다.

embrace ~를 품에 안다

주격관계대명사 that:
그를 개선하고 정화해줄
조용하고 충실한 고통

at the height of
~의 절정에, 한창일 때

emptiness toward the planet, but at the instant of leaping "it's impossible" flashed once more through his mind. There he lay on the shore, shattered. He had not understood how to love. If at the instant of leaping he **had had** the strength of faith in the fulfillment of his love he **would have soared** into the heights and been united with the star.

"Love must not entreat 간청하다," she added, "or demand. Love must have the strength to become certain within itself. Then it ceases merely to be attracted and begins to attract. Sinclair, your love is attracted to me. Once it begins to attract me, I will come. I will not make a gift of myself, I must be won."

Another time she told me a different story, concerning a lover whose love was unrequited. He withdrew completely within himself, believing his love would consume 소모시키다 him. The world became lost to him, he no longer noticed blue sky and green woods, he no longer heard the brook murmur; his ears had turned deaf to the notes of the harp: nothing mattered any more; he had become poor and wretched 비참한. Yet his love increased and he would rather have died or been ruined than renounce possessing this beautiful woman. Then he felt that his passion had consumed everything else within him and become so strong, **so** magnetic **that** the beautiful woman must follow. She came to him and he stood with outstretched arms ready to draw her to him. As she stood before him she was completely transformed and with awe he felt and saw that he had won back all he had previously lost. She stood before him and surrendered herself to him and sky, forest, and brook all came toward him in new and resplendent 눈부신 colors, belonged to him, and spoke to him in his own

at the instant of
~하려는 순간에
flash 갑자기 마음에 떠오르다

there ~ shattered 강기슭에
떨어져 몸이 으스러지다

가정법 과거완료: 만약
~했더라면, ~했을 텐데

it=love 사랑은 끌려가기를
중단하고 끌어당기기 시작하다

내 자신이 너의 선물로 가는
것이 아니라, (네가 나를
간절히 원했기 때문에) 너는
나를 성취한 것이다.

unrequited
보답이 없는, 일방적인

그에게 세상이 사라졌다.

지각동사+목+목/보(동):
hear ~ murmur
시냇물이 속삭이는 것을 듣다

renounce=give up having

so ~ that 구조:
끌어당기는 힘이 너무 강해서
결국 ~하게 되다

with awe 경외감으로

language. And instead of merely winning a woman he embraced the entire world and every star in heaven glowed within him and sparkled with joy in his soul. He had loved and had found himself. But most people love to lose themselves.

My love for Frau Eva seemed to fill my whole life. But every day it manifested 나타내다 itself differently. Sometimes I felt certain **that** it was not she as a person whom I was attracted to and yearned for with all my being, but **that** she existed only as a metaphor 상징 of my inner self, a metaphor whose sole purpose was to lead me more deeply into myself. Things she said often sounded like replies from my subconscious 무의식 to questions **that** tormented 괴롭히다 me. There were other moments when I sat beside her and burned with sensual desire 관능적 욕구 and kissed objects she had touched. And little by little, sensual and spiritual love, reality and symbol began to overlap. Then it would happen that as I thought about her in my room at home in tranquil intimacy I felt her hand in mine and her lips touching my lips. Or I would be at her house, would look into her face and hear her voice, yet not know whether she was real or a dream. I began to sense how one can possess a love constantly and eternally. I would have an insight while reading a book — and this would feel the same as Eva's kiss. She caressed 쓰다듬다 my hair and smiled at me affectionately 애정을 담아 and this felt like taking a step forward within myself. Everything significant and full of fate for me adopted her form. She could transform herself into any of my thoughts and each of my thoughts could be transformed into her.

I had been apprehensive about the Christmas vacation — to be spent at my parents' house — because I thought

- 165 -

it would be agony to be away from Frau Eva for two whole weeks. But it did not turn out like that. It was wonderful to be at home and yet be able to think of her. When I arrived back in H. I waited two more days before going to see her, so as to savor this security, this **being** independent of her physical presence. I had dreams, too, in which my union with her was consummated in new symbolic acts. She was an ocean into which I streamed. She was a star and I another on my way to her, circling round each other. I told her this dream when I first visited her again.

"The dream is beautiful," she said quietly. "Make it come true."

There came a day in early spring **that** I have never forgotten. I entered the hallway, a window was open and a stream of air let in the heavy fragrance of the hyacinths. As no one was about, I went upstairs to Max Demian's study. I tapped lightly on the door and, as was my custom, went in without waiting for a reply.

The room was dark, all the curtains were drawn. The door to the small adjoining room stood open. There Max had set up a chemical laboratory. That's where the only light came from. I thought no one was in and drew back one of the curtains.

Then I saw Max slumped on a stool by the curtained window, looking oddly changed, and it flashed through me: You've seen this before! His arms hung limp, hands in his lap 무릎, his head bent slightly forward, and his eyes, though open, were unseeing and dead; in one of his pupils 동공 **as in** a piece of glass a thin, harsh ray of light snapped the lens open and shut, open and shut. The wan 창백한 face was absorbed in itself and without expression, except for its immense rigidity 엄청난 경직; he

savor this security
이 안정감을 음미하기 위해서
this (=security) being:
그녀의 육체로부터의 독립을
의미하는 이 안정감
be consummated in ~ acts
~한 행위로 완성되다
생략구조:
I (was) another (star)

a day that ~한 날이 왔다

let in ~ hyacinths
히아신스 꽃의 짙은 향기를
창문 안으로 불어 넣다

adjoining room 옆방

see ~ slumped
털썩 주저앉아 있는 것을 보다
it flashed through me:
어떤 생각이 번개처럼 내
머리를 스치고 지나갔다.
hang limp 축 늘어져 있다.

as in ~에서처럼
harsh ray of light 강한 빛
렌즈를 열었다 닫았다 하기를
반복했다.
be absorbed in itself
생각에 잠겨있다. 침잠하다

resembled an age-old animal mask at the portal 입구 of a temple. He did not seem to breathe.

Overcome by dread, I quietly left the room and walked downstairs. In the hallway I met Frau Eva, pale and seemingly tired, which I had never known her to be before. Just then a shadow passed over the window, the white glare of the sun suddenly fled.

glare 섬광, 번쩍이는 빛

"I was in Max's room," I whispered rapidly. "Has something happened? He's either asleep or lost within himself, I don't know which; I saw him look like that once before."

see ~ look like

"You didn't wake him, did you?" she quickly asked.

"No. He didn't hear me. I left the room immediately. Tell me, what is the matter with him?"

She swept the back of her hand once across her brow.

She swept ~ her brow
손등으로 이마를 닦다

"Don't worry, Sinclair, nothing will happen to him. He has withdrawn. It will soon pass."

He has withdrawn.
=he fell into himself.
침잠하다: 마음을 차분히
가라앉히고 사색하거나 자신의
세계에 몰입하다.

She stood up and went out into the garden — although it was beginning to rain. I felt that she did not want me to accompany her and so I walked up and down the hallway, inhaled the bewildering scent of the hyacinths, stared at my bird picture above the doorway, and breathed the stifling atmosphere that filled the house that morning. What was it? What had happened?

inhale ~ 히아신스의 매혹적인
향기를 들이마시다

stifling 숨 막힐 듯한

Frau Eva returned before long. Raindrops clung to her black hair. She sat down in her armchair. She seemed weary. I stepped up to her, bent over her head, and kissed the rain out of her hair. Her eyes were bright and calm but the raindrops tasted like tears.

"Should I go and see how he is?" I asked in a whisper.

She smiled weakly.

"Don't be a little boy, Sinclair!" she admonished me, loudly as though trying to break a spell within herself.

admonish 훈계하다, 타이르다
break a spell
마법/주문을 풀다

"Get along now and come back later. I can't talk to you now."

I half walked, half ran from the house and the town, toward the mountains. The fine rain slanted into my face, low clouds swept by **as though** weighed down with fear. Near the ground there was hardly a breath of air but in the higher altitudes 고도 a storm seemed to rage. Several times the lurid sun broke briefly through harsh rifts in the steel-gray clouds.

Then a loose, yellow cloud swept across the sky, collided with the other, gray bank of cloud. In a few seconds the wind had fashioned a shape out of this yellow and blue-gray mass, a gigantic 거대한 bird that tore itself free of the steel-blue chaos and flew off into the sky with a great beating of wings. Then the storm became audible and rain rattled down mixed with hail. A brief, incredible, terrifying roar of thunder cracked across the rain-lashed landscape and immediately afterwards a gleam of sunshine burst through. On the nearby mountains the pale snow shone livid and unreal above the brown forest.

When, hours later, I returned wet and wind-blown, Demian himself opened the door.

He took me up to his room. A gas jet was burning in his laboratory and papers were strewn about the floor. He had evidently been working.

"Sit down," he invited, "you must be exhausted, it was horrible weather. One can see that you really were outside. There'll be tea in a moment."

"Something is the matter today," I began hesitantly. "It can't only be a thunderstorm 폭풍우."

He looked at me inquiringly 탐색하듯.

"Did you see something?"

slant into my face
비스듬히 내 얼굴을 때리다
sweep by 스쳐 지나가다
as though (they were)
weighed down with fear
두려움으로 압박을 받은 듯
rage 불어 닥치다

the lurid sun ~ clouds
생기를 잃은 태양은 (푸른빛이
도는) 회색 구름의 거친 틈을
통해 잠시 반짝였다.

collide with ~와 충돌하다
bank of cloud 구름 층

tear oneself free of
~로부터 박차고 나오다

audible 들을 수 있는
rain rattled ~ hail
비가 우박과 섞여 타다닥
소리를 내며 쏟아지다
terrifying roar ~ landscape
무시한 천둥소리가 빗발치는
풍경을 가로질러 지나가다

shine livid and unreal
창백하고 비현실적으로 빛나다

gas jet 가스 불꽃

strew-strewed-strewn
흩뿌리다, strewn 흩어진

something is the matter
오늘 뭔가가 이상해.

"Yes. I saw a picture in the clouds, quite clearly for a moment."

"What kind of picture?"

"It was a bird."

"The sparrow hawk? Your dream bird?"

"Yes, it was my sparrow hawk. It was yellow and gigantic and it flew off into the blue-black clouds."

Demian heaved a great sigh.

heave a great sigh
깊은 한숨을 내쉬다

There was a knock on the door. The old servant brought in the tea.

"Help yourself, Sinclair, please. I don't believe you saw the bird just by chance."

by chance 우연히

"By chance? Does one get to see such things by chance?"

"Quite right. No, one doesn't. The bird has a significance 의미. Do you know what?"

"No. I only feel that it signifies some shattering event, a move on the part of destiny. I believe that it concerns all of us."

signify 의미하다, 나타내다
shattering=destructive
concern 관련이 있다

He was pacing excitedly back and forth.

"A move on the part of destiny!" he shouted. "I dreamed the same kind of thing last night and my mother had a presentiment 예감 yesterday which conveyed the same message. I dreamed I was climbing up a ladder placed against a tree trunk or tower. When I reached the top I saw the whole landscape ablaze 타오르는— a vast plain with innumerable towns and villages. I can't tell you the whole dream yet, everything is still somewhat confused."

convey 전달하다

"Do you feel that the dream concerns you personally?"

"Of course. No one dreams anything that doesn't 'concern him personally.' But it doesn't concern me only, you're right. I differentiate quite sharply between dreams that reveal movements within my own soul and

differentiate between A and B: A와 B를 정확히 구분하다

the other, far rarer dreams **in which** the fate of all mankind suggests itself. I have rarely had such dreams and never before one of which I could say that it was a prophecy 예언 which was fulfilled. The interpretations 해석 are too uncertain. But I know for sure that I have dreamed something that doesn't concern me alone. **For** this dream links up with others, previous dreams I have had, **to which** it is a sequel. These are the dreams, Sinclair, which fill me with the forebodings 예감 I've spoken of to you. We both know that the world is quite rotten 썩은 but that wouldn't be any reason to predict its imminent collapse or something of the kind. But for several years I have had dreams **from which** I conclude, or which make me feel, that the collapse of an old world is indeed Imminent. At first these were weak and remote intimations 먼 암시 but they have become increasingly stronger and more distinct. I still know nothing except that something is going to happen on a vast scale, something dreadful in which I myself will be involved. Sinclair, we will take part in this event that we have discussed so often. The world wants to renew itself. There's a smell of death in the air. Nothing can be born without first dying. But it is far more terrible than I had thought."

I stared at him aghast 놀라서.

"Can't you tell me the rest of your dream?" I asked shyly.

He shook his head.

"No."

The door opened to let in Frau Eva.

"You're not feeling sad, I hope."

She looked refreshed, all trace of fatigue had vanished. Demian smiled at her and she came up to us as a

---

far rarer dreams
훨씬 더 진기한 꿈
in which =where 꿈에서
suggest itself
스스로를 암시하다
=and (I have) never before
(had) one of such dreams
(that) I could say that it ~
나는 성취된 예언이었다고
말할 만한 그런 꿈은 전에 한
번도 꾼 적이 없어.
접속사 for: 왜냐하면
link up with ~와 관계가 있다
=are concerned with
to which=and it is a sequel
to the previous dreams
그것은 ~의 속편/후편이다

imminent collapse
=impending destruction
임박한 붕괴
from which
=and from the dreams

on a vast scale
거대한 규모로
be involved in
~와 관련이 있다

all trace of ~ vanished
모든 피로의 흔적이 사라지다

mother approaches frightened children.

"No, we are not sad, mother. We've merely tried to puzzle out these new omens. But it's no use anyway. Whatever happens will suddenly be here; then we shall learn soon enough what we need to know."

puzzle ~ 이 새로운 징조들에 대한 수수께끼를 풀다

But I felt dispirited 의기소침한, and when I took my leave and walked alone through the hallway, the stale scent of the hyacinths seemed cadaverous. A shadow had fallen over us.

stale=not fresh 진부한

cadaverous 시체와 같은

Chapter VIII
The End begins

8. The End Begins

I had persuaded my parents to allow me the summer
semester in H. My friends and I now spent almost all our
time in the garden by the river instead of the house.
The Japanese, who had been duly beaten in the boxing
match, had departed; the disciple of Tolstoi had gone,
too. Demian kept a horse and went for long rides day
after day. I was frequently alone with his mother.

be duly beaten in
~에서 완전히 패배하다

There were times when I was simply astonished how
peaceful my life had become. I had **so** long been
accustomed to being alone, to leading a life of self-denial
자제, to battling strenuously with my agonizing difficulties,
that these months in H. seemed to me altogether like a
magic dream island on which I was allowed to lead a
comfortable, enchanted existence among beautiful and
agreeable surroundings. I had a presentiment 예감 that
this was a foretaste 전조 of that new and higher
community which we speculated 추측하다 about so much.
Yet at any moment this happiness could produce in me
the deepest melancholy 우울, for I knew very well that it
could not last. It was not my lot 운명 to breathe fullness
and comfort, I needed the spur 자극 of tormented haste.
I felt that one day I would waken from these beloved
images of beauty and stand, alone again, in the cold
world **where** there was nothing for me but solitude 고독
and struggle — neither peace nor relaxation 휴식, no easy
living together.

self-denial 자제, 극기, 금욕
be accustomed to ~ing
~에 익숙하다

so ~ that 구조

enchanted existence
황홀한 생활

at any moment 언젠가

spur of tormented haste
고통스러운 탐험이란 자극
haste=expedition

관계부사 where=in which
but=except (for)

At those moments I would nestle with redoubled
affection close to Frau Eva, **glad** that my fate still bore
these beautiful calm features.

nestle close to
~에게 정답게 바싹 다가가다
(being) glad 분사구:
~에 기뻐하면서

The summer weeks passed quickly and uneventfully,
the semester was nearly over and it would soon be time

uneventfully
무사히, (특별한) 사건 없이

for me to leave. I dared not think of it, but clung to each beautiful day **as** the butterfly clings to his honeyed flower. This had been my happy time, life's first fulfillment, my acceptance into this intimate, elect circle — what was to follow? I would battle through again, suffer the old longings, dream dreams, be alone.

접속사 as: ~하듯

elect=chosen 선택받은

One day foreboding 예감 came over me with **such** force **that** my love for Frau Eva suddenly flared up painful within me. My God, how soon I must leave here, see her no more, no longer hear her dear assured 확고한 steps throughout the house, no longer find her flowers on my table! And what had I achieved? I had dreamed, had luxuriated in dreams and contentment 만족, instead of winning her, instead of struggling to clasp her forever to myself! Everything she had told me about genuine love came back to me, a hundred delicate admonitions, **as** many gentle enticements 유혹, promises perhaps — what had I made of them? Nothing. Absolutely nothing!

such ~ that 구조

flare up painful(ly)
고통스럽게 불타오르다

luxuriate in=enjoy
~를 즐기다

delicate admonitions, as
~로써 해준 세심한 충고들

them=admonitions
what had I made of them?
그것들로부터 나는 무엇을
이룰 수 있었던가?

I went to the center of my room and stood still, **endeavoring** to concentrate 집중하다 the whole of my consciousness on Frau Eva, **summoning** all the strength in my soul to let her feel my love and draw her to me. She must come, she must long for my embrace, my kiss must tremble insatiably 탐욕스럽게 on her ripe lips.

분사구 endeavoring:
~에 집중하려고 노력하면서
분사구 summoning:
모든 힘을 불러 모아서
사역동사+목+보(동):
let ~ feel and draw

I stood and concentrated every energy until I could feel cold creeping up my fingers and toes. I felt strength radiating 발산하다 from me. For a few moments I felt something contract 수축하다 within me, something bright and cool which felt like a crystal in my heart — I knew it was my ego. The chill crept up to my chest.

지각동사+목+목/보(ing):
feel ~ creeping up
feel ~ radiating
feel ~ contract

creep up 살며시 올라가다

Relaxed from this terrible tension I felt that something was about to happen. I was mortally exhausted but I was ready to behold 보다 Eva step into the room, radiant and

relaxed from ~에서 진정되자

mortally exhausted
죽을 만큼 지친/피곤한

(being) radiant and ecstatic

ecstatic 불타는 황홀한 기분이 되어.

The clattering of hooves could be heard approaching along the street. It sounded near and metallic, then suddenly stopped. I leaped to the window and saw Demian dismounting 내리다 below. I ran down.

"What is it, Demian?"

He paid no attention to my words. He was very pale and sweat poured down his cheeks. He tied the bridle 고삐 of his steaming horse to the garden fence and took my arm and walked down the street with me.

"Have you heard about it?"

I had heard nothing.

Demian squeezed my arm and turned his face toward me, with a strangely somber yet sympathetic look in his eyes.

"Yes, it's starting. You've heard about the difficulties with Russia."

"What? Is it war?"

He spoke very softly although no one was anywhere near us.

"It hasn't been declared yet. But there will be war. You can take my word for that. I didn't want to worry you but I have seen omens 전조 on three different occasions since that time. So it won't be the end of the world, no earthquake, no revolution, but war. You'll see what a sensation 대사건 that will be! People will love it. Even now they can hardly wait for the killing to begin — their lives are that dull! But you will see, Sinclair, that this is only the beginning. Perhaps it will be a very big war, a war on a gigantic scale. But that, too, will only be the beginning. The new world has begun and the new world will be terrible for those clinging to the old. What will you do?"

clattering of hooves
달각거리는 말발굽소리

지각동사+목+목/보(ing)
see ~ dismounting

squeeze=hold tight

somber=gloomy 침울한
sympathetic 연민에 찬

declare 선포하다

take=believe

can hardly wait for
~를 학수고대하고 있다
that dull 그만큼 지루한

for those (who are) ~ old
낡은 것에 매달린 사람에게는

I was dumfounded 말문이 막힌, it all sounded so strange, so improbable 사실 같지 않은.

"I don't know ― and you?"

He shrugged his shoulders.

"I'll be called up as soon as the mobilization order comes through. I'm a lieutenant."

"You, a lieutenant! I had no idea."

"Yes, that was one of the ways I compromised 타협하다. You know I dislike calling attention to myself so much I almost always went to the other extreme, just to give a correct impression. I believe I'll be on the front in a week."

"My God."

"Now don't get sentimental 감상적인. Of course it's not going to be any fun **ordering** men to fire on living beings, but that will be incidental. Each of us will be caught up in the great chain of events. You, too, you'll be drafted, for sure."

"And what about your mother, Demian?"

Only now my thoughts turned back to what had happened a quarter of an hour before. How the world had changed in the meantime! I had summoned all my strength to conjure up the sweetest of images and now fate looked at me suddenly with a threatening and horrible mask.

"My mother? We don't have to worry about her. She is safe, safer than anyone else in the world today. Do you love her that much?"

"Didn't you know?"

He laughed lightly, relieved 안심하며.

"Of course I knew. No one has called my mother Frau Eva who hasn't been in love with her. You either called me or her today."

be called up 징병 당하다
mobilization order 동원령
lieutenant (육군) 중위, 소위

dislike calling ~ to myself
내 자신에게로 주의가
환기되는 것을 싫어하다
(눈에 띄는 행동을 싫어하다)
go to the other extreme
정반대의 행동을 취하다
be on the front
전선/전쟁터에 나가다

가주어 it, 진주어(ordering)
A에게 B하라고 명령하는 것은
ordering=to order
fire on living beings
살아있는 자에게 총을 겨누다
incidental 부차적인
be drafted 징집되다

in the meantime 그 사이에

conjure up 떠올리다

"Yes, I called her."

"She felt it. She sent me away all of a sudden, saying I would have to go see you. I had just told her the news about Russia."

We turned around and exchanged a few words more. Demian untied his horse and mounted.

Only upstairs in my room did I realize how much Demian's news, and still more the previous strain, had exhausted me. But Frau Eva had heard me! My thoughts had reached her heart. She would have come herself — if. . . How curious all this was, and, fundamentally, how beautiful! And now there was to be war. What we had talked about so often was to begin. Demian had known so much about it ahead of time. How strange **that** the stream of the world was not to bypass us any more, **that** it now went straight through our hearts, and **that** now or very soon the moment would come when the world would need us, when it would seek to transform itself. Demian was right, one could not be sentimental about that. The only remarkable thing was that I was to share the very personal matter of my fate with so many others, with the whole world in fact. Well, so be it! I was prepared. When I walked through town in the evening every street corner was buzzing, everywhere the word was war.

I went to Frau Eva's. We ate supper in the summer house. I was the only guest. No one said a word about the war. Only later on, shortly before I was to leave, Frau Eva said: "Dear Sinclair, you called me today. You know why I didn't come myself. But don't forget: you know the call now and whenever you need someone who bears the sign, you can appeal to me."

She rose to her feet and preceded me into the garden

---

only upstairs *did I realize*

still more the strain
그 이전의 긴장

fundamentally 본질적으로

was to be=would be 예정

(가주어 it+be) 생략구조:
How strange (it was) that

bypass 우회하다
it=the stream of the world
go straight through
~를 관통하다
관계부사절 도치구조:
the moment ~ when
~할 순간이 올 것이다
it=the world

was to=must
share A with B:
A와 B를 공유하다

Well, so be it!
그렇게 흘러가도록 두라!

buzzing 사람들로 들끓다

appeal to
~에게 도움을 청하다
precede A into B
A보다 먼저 일어나 B로 나가다

twilight. Tall and regal 당당한 she strode between the silent trees.

I am coming to the end of my story. Everything went very rapidly from then on. Soon there was war, and Demian, strangely unfamiliar in his uniform, left us. I accompanied his mother home. It was not long before I, too, took my leave of her. She kissed me on the mouth and clasped me for a moment to her breast. Her great eyes burned close and firmly into mine.

All men seemed to have become brothers — overnight. They talked of "the fatherland" and of "honor," but what lay behind it was their own fate whose unveiled face they had now all beheld for one brief moment. Young men left their barracks, were packed into trains, and on many faces I saw a sign — not ours — but a beautiful, dignified sign nonetheless **that** meant love and death. I, too, was embraced by people **whom** I had never seen before and I understood this gesture and responded to it. Intoxication made them do it, not a hankering after their destiny. But this intoxication was sacred, for it was the result of their all having thrown that brief and terribly disquieting glance into the eyes of their fate.

It was nearly winter when I was sent to the front 전방. Despite the excitement of being under fire for the first time, in the beginning everything disappointed me. At one time I had given much thought to why men were so very rarely capable of living for an ideal 이상. Now I saw that many, no, all men were capable of dying for one. Yet it could not be a personal, a freely chosen ideal; it had to be one mutually accepted.

As time went on though I realized I had underestimated these men. **However** much mutual service and danger made a uniform mass of them, I still saw many approach

(Being) tall and regal
stride-strode-stridden
성큼 성큼 걷다

it is not long before ~
머지않아 ~하다

what lay ~ moment
그 이면에는 그들 자신의
운명이 있었고, 그들은 짧은
순간 동안 자신의 운명의
드러난 모습을 보았던 것이다.

barrack 막사, 병영

주격관계대명사 that

목적격관계대명사 whom

hanker after=long for
intoxication 술기운, 도취

throw A into B: A를 B
속으로 던지다
terribly disquieting glance
지독하게 불안한 시선

one=ideal 이상

(관/대+be) 생략구조:
one (that was) mutually ~
상호 수용된 이상

a uniform mass of them
획일화된 무리

the will of fate with great dignity. Many, very many, not only during the attack but at every moment of the day, wore in their eyes the remote, resolute, somewhat possessed look **which** knows nothing of aims and signified 의미하다 complete surrender to the incredible. **Whatever** they might think or believe, they were ready, they could be used, they were the clay **of which** the future could be shaped. The more single-mindedly 한결같이 the world concentrated on war and heroism, on honor and other old ideals, the more remote and improbable any whisper of genuine humanity sounded — **that** was all just surface, in the same way that the question of the war's external and political objectives 목적 remained superficial. Deep down, underneath, something was taking shape. Something akin to a new humanity 인간애. For I could see many men — and many died beside me — who had begun to feel acutely 예리하게 that hatred and rage, slaughter 학살 and annihilation 전멸, were not bound up with these objectives. No, these objectives and aims were completely fortuitous 우연한. The most primitive 원시의, even the wildest feelings were not directed at the enemy; their bloody task was merely an irradiation 발산 of the soul, of the soul divided within itself, **which** filled them with the lust to rage and kill, annihilate 소멸시키다 and die **so that** they might be born anew.

One night in early spring I stood guard in front of a farm that we had occupied. A listless wind was blowing fitfully; across the Flemish sky cloud armies 구름 떼 rode on high, somewhere behind them the suggestion 암시 of a moon. I had been uneasy the entire day - something was worrying me deeply. Now on my dark guard post 초소 I fervently 열렬히 recalled the images of my life and thought of Frau Eva and of Demian. I stood braced

---

see ~ approach
many wore ~ look
많은 사람들이 -한 눈빛을
지녔다.

somewhat possessed look
다소 홀린 듯한 눈빛

그 진흙(=그들)으로 미래가
빚어지다
be shaped of ~로 형성되다
the more A, **the more** B
A하면 할수록 더욱 B 하다

sound improbable
거짓말 같이 들리다
improbable 참말 같지 않은
that=genuine humanity
in the same way that
~와 마찬가지로
remain superficial
피상적이다

akin to ~와 유사한
humanity 인간성, 박애

be bound up with
~와 밀접한 관계가 있다

관계대명사 which
=and the soul fill A with B:
그리고 영혼은 A를 B로 채우다
lust to ~하려는 욕망
so that: ~하기 위해서

stand guard 보초를 서다

listless 무기력한, 나른한
blow fitfully
변덕스럽게 간간이 불어오다
Flemish 플랑드르의

stand braced against
~에 기대어 서 있다

against a poplar tree **staring** into the drifting clouds **whose** mysteriously writhing patches of light soon metamorphosed into huge series of swirling 소용돌이치는 images. From the strange weakness of my pulse, the insensitiveness 무감각 of my skin to wind and rain, and my intense state of consciousness I could sense that a master was near me.

A huge city could be seen in the clouds out of which millions of people streamed in a host over vast landscapes. Into their midst *stepped* a mighty, godlike figure, as huge as a mountain range, with sparkling stars in her hair, bearing the features of Frau Eva. The ranks 대열 of the people were swallowed up into her **as** into a giant cave and vanished from sight. The goddess cowered 웅크리다 on the ground, the mark **luminous** on her forehead. A dream seemed to hold sway over her: she closed her eyes and her countenance 안색 became twisted with pain. Suddenly she cried out and from her forehead sprang stars, many thousands of shining stars **that** leaped in marvelous arches and semicircles across the black sky.

One of these stars shot straight toward me with a clear ringing sound and it seemed to seek me out. Then it burst asunder with a roar 굉음 into a thousand sparks, tore me aloft 높이 and smashed me back to the ground again, the world shattered above me with a thunderous roar.

They found me near the poplar tree, covered with earth and with many wounds.

I lay in a cellar 지하실, guns roared above me. I lay in a wagon and jolted across the empty fields. Mostly I was asleep or unconscious. But **the more** deeply I slept **the more** strongly I felt **that** something was drawing me on,

분사구 staring into:
흘러가는 구름을 응시하며
관계대명사 whose:
그리고 그 구름을 통해 나오는 신비롭게 몸부림치는 빛의 조각들이 ~로 변했다
metamorphose into
=change into
from ~ consciousness, I could sense that ~로부터 나는 느낄 수 있었다

stream in a host
무리 지어 쏟아져 나오다
주어+동사 도치구조
Into their midst *stepped a might, godlike figure*

as into ~
마치 ~속으로 삼켜진 것처럼

(being) 분사구 생략구조:
=the mark (being) luminous on her forehead
hold sway over ~를 지배하다

주격 관/대 that: 수천의 반짝이는 별들이 멋진 활 모양으로 반원을 그리며 검은 하늘 전체로 퍼져나갔다
leap 뛰어오르다, 도약하다

burst asunder into ~
산산이 부서져 ~가 되다
smash 내동댕이치다

shatter 산산이 부서지다
thunderous 우레 같은

jolt 덜거덕 거리며 가다

the more, the more 구조

- 180 -

that I was following a force that had mastery over me.

I lay in a stable 마구간, on straw. It was dark and someone had stepped on my hand. But something inside me wanted to keep going and I was drawn on more forcefully than ever, Again I lay in a wagon and later on a stretcher 들것 or ladder. More strongly than ever I felt myself being summoned somewhere, felt nothing but this urge that I must finally get there.

Then I reached my goal. It was night and I was fully conscious. I had just felt the urge pulling mightily within me: now I was in a long hall, bedded down on the floor. I felt I had reached the destination which had summoned me. I turned my head: close to my mattress lay another; someone on it bent forward and looked at me. He had the sign on his forehead. It was Max Demian.

I was unable to speak and he could not or did not want to either. He just looked at me. The light from a bulb strung on the wall above him played down on his face. He smiled.

He gazed into my eyes for what seemed an endless time. Slowly he brought his face closer to mine: we almost touched.

"Sinclair," he said in a whisper.

I told him with a glance that I heard.

He smiled again, almost as with pity.

"Little fellow," he said, smiling.

His lips lay very close to mine. Quietly he continued to speak.

"Can you remember Franz Kromer?" he asked,

I blinked at him and smiled, too.

"Little Sinclair, listen: I will have to go away. Perhaps you'll need me again sometime, against Kromer or something. If you call me then I won't come crudely, on

have mastery over
~를 지배하다

step on ~를 밟고 지나가다

지각동사+목+목/보(ing):
feel ~ being summoned
~로 소환되는 것을 느끼다
nothing but=only

feel ~ pulling

be bedded ~ floor
바닥에 눕혀져 있다

bend forward
앞으로 몸을 숙이다

a bulb (which was) strung
벽에 매달린/묶인 전구
string-strung-strung

for what ~ time 영원처럼
느껴지는 긴 시간 동안

come crudely 매우 거칠게
(=절실하게) 달려오다

horseback or by train. You'll have to listen within yourself, then you will notice that I am within you. Do you understand? And something else. Frau Eva said that if ever you were in a bad way I was to give you a kiss from her that she sends by me. . . Close your eyes, Sinclair!"

be in a bad way
잘 지내지 못하다
was to=should

I closed my eyes in obedience 순종하며. I felt a light kiss on my lips where there was always a little fresh blood which never would go away. And then I fell asleep.

Next morning someone woke me: I had to have my wounds dressed. When I was finally wide awake I turned quickly to the mattress next to mine. On it lay a stranger I'd never seen before.

사역동사+목+목/보(pp):
have ~ dressed
붕대를 감아야 했다

Dressing the wound hurt. Everything that has happened to me since has hurt. But sometimes when I find the key and climb deep into myself where the images of fate lie aslumber in the dark mirror, I need only bend over that dark mirror to behold my own image, now completely resembling him, my brother, my master.

hurt 아프다

lie aslumber=lie asleep

him=Demian